Dimitri Mitropoulos. Photo Roberts, Minneapolis circa 1946
(coll. S.A. Arfanis)

THE COMPLETE DISCOGRAPHY

OF

DIMITRI MITROPOULOS

COMPILED BY STATHIS A. ARFANIS
RESEARCH ASSOCIATE NICK NICKSON

Published by IRINNA S.A.

Athens 1990

CONTENTS

"The Complete Discography of Dimitri Mitropoulos" was published in Athens in December 1990 by IRINNA S.A. - Special Publications in 2000 copies.

Printing: Thanassis Petroulakis S.A.
Colour reproduction: C. Alexandris - S. Papadopoulos
Text editing supervisor: Yannis Prezanis
Phototypesetting: FOTRON S.A.

Art Director: Popi Tsakiraki - IRINNA

Photographs of record sleeves from the
S.A. Arfanis record collection.

© Copyright: S.A. Arfanis & IRINNA S.A. Special Publications
36, Voucourestiou str. Athens 106 74 Greece. Tel. 3646.589

ISBN 960-7110-00-5

to Crysta

ΠΡΟΛΟΓΟΣ

Με τιμά και με ευχαριστεί ιδιαίτερα η πρόσκληση του κ. Αρφάνη να γράψω έναν πρόλογο σ' αυτήν που θεωρώ ως μια από τις πληρέστερες δισκογραφίες που έχουν γίνει ποτέ για έναν καλλιτέχνη.

Άρχισα την συλλογή δίσκων μου στα πρώτα χρόνια της δεκαετίας του '40, την εποχή ακριβώς που η Columbia έθετε σε κυκλοφορία τον πρώτο δίσκο του μεγάλου Δημήτρη Μητρόπουλου, την εισαγωγή Κοριολανός, την οποία σύντομα ακολούθησε η 6η Συμφωνία «Ποιμενική» του Μπετόβεν.

Απο την εποχή των 78 στροφών μέχρι τις 45 και τον δίσκο μακράς διαρκείας, πολλές λαμπρές εκτελέσεις από την Συμφωνική Ορχήστρα της Μιννεάπολης και αργότερα, από την Φιλαρμονική της Νέας Υόρκης ήλθαν να επιβεβαιώσουν την γνώμη που είχα σχηματίσει για το ανάστημα του Μαέστρου και την ικανότητά του να κάνει την μουσική να ηχεί συναρπαστική και απολαυστική.

Τώρα που έχουν περάσει τριάντα χρόνια από τον θάνατό του και ακόμη περισσότερα από την τελευταία του εμπορική ηχογράφηση, η εφεύρεση του δίσκου Compact μας δίνει την δυνατότητα να ανατρέξουμε στις ραδιοφωνικές του αναμεταδόσεις και ζωντανές εκτελέσεις, που γιά καλή μας τύχη κάποιες αφοσιωμένες ψυχές κατέγραψαν, αρχικά σε πρότυπους δίσκους (acetates) και αργότερα σε μαγνητοταινίες, ώστε να μπορούμε εμείς τώρα να τις έχουμε στην πιο σύγχρονη μορφή και να τις απολαμβάνουμε όσο ποτέ άλλοτε.

Θεωρώ αυτήν την προσπάθεια ως άλλον ένα τρόπο για να πούμε όλοι εμείς «ευχαριστώ» στόν Μαέστρο, τιμώντας την μνήμη του.

Προσωπικά τον γνώρισα όταν ήλθε με την Φιλαρμονική της Νέας Υόρκης, κατά την διάρκεια της περιοδείας στήν Πολιτεία μας, τον Απρίλιο του 1957. Το πρωί της 14ης Απριλίου, μαζί με τον διευθυντή του Δημοτικού Μουσικού Συλλόγου, του οργανισμού που χρηματοδότησε την εκδήλωση στο Rochester, πήγαμε στο σιδηροδρομικό σταθμό για να υποδεχτούμε αυτόν και την ορχήστρα και να τον συνοδεύσουμε στο ξενοδοχείο. Μετά από την συναυλία που δόθηκε στο θέατρο Ήστμαν εκείνο το απόγευμα και ακούστηκε και από το ραδιόφωνο, μέλη της Ελληνικής Ορθόδοξης Εκκλησίας έδωσαν δεξίωση προς τιμήν του, της οποίας είχα το προνόμιο να προΐσταμαι.

Ήταν πολύ κουρασμένος από το ταξίδι και εξαντλημένος από την απογευματινή συναυλία, όμως η γοητεία του και το ενδιαφέρον του για εκείνους που περίμεναν να τον καλωσορίσουν έμειναν αξέχαστα.

Σήμερα που όλο και περισσότεροι φιλόμουσοι, μουσικοί, συλλέκτες και ιστορικοί αρχίζουν να αντιλαμβάνονται το πραγματικό μέγεθος των χαρισμάτων αυτού του ανθρώπου, μπορούμε να ελπίζουμε σε μια ακόμη βαθύτερη συνειδητοποίηση εκ μέρους τους, του μοναδικού του ταλέντου που εξακολουθεί να λάμπει μέσα από κάθε εκτέλεση που μας άφησε για να μπορούμε να την χαιρόμαστε ξανά και ξανά.

Ουσιαστικά, αποτελούσε πρότυπο εκείνης της καλλιτεχνικής ακεραιότητας που έκανε την Αρχαία Ελλάδα τόσο μεγάλη. Και πράγματι, ένιωθε υπερήφανος που ήταν τέκνο της Ελληνικής και συνεπώς της Παγκόσμιας παράδοσης. Η αφοσίωσή του και η ικανότητά του να δίνει νέα «πνοή» στην μουσική που διηύθυνε είναι αναμφισβήτητες. Χωρίς αμφιβολία, υπήρξε ένας από τους μεγάλους αρχιμουσικούς του καιρού μας.

Nick Nickson
Rochester, New York
Δεκέμβριος, 1990

6

OVERTURE

I am deeply honored and feel a great pleasure in being invited by Mr. Arfanis to write an introduction to what I consider to be one of the most thorough discographies ever accorded a recording artist.

I began my record collection in the early forties, just when Columbia was releasing the first of the great Dimitri Mitropoulos records ... the Coriolan Overture, which was followed by the Beethoven Sixth Symphony, soon after.

From the days of the 78s to the 45s and the Long Play disc, many a sparkling performance from the Minneapolis Symphony, and later the New York Philharmonic was to secure my feeling about the enormous stature of Maestro Mitropoulos and his ability to make music sound exciting and exhilarating.

Now, thirty years since his passing, and even longer since his last commercial recording, the advent of the Compact Disc has enabled us to go back to his radio broadcasts and live performances, which we are lucky to have had some diligent souls put on acetate discs and later on tape, so that we can now have them in the most modern format to enjoy more than ever.

I consider this effort to be another way for us all to say "Thank you" to the Maestro, by honoring his memory.

I personally met him when he came through with the New York Philharmonic during the Upstate Tour in April of 1957. On the morning of April 14, the manager of the sponsoring organization in Rochester, the Civic Music Association, and I, drove to the train station to welcome him and the orchestra and then take him to the hotel. Following the broadcast concert given in the Eastman Theater that afternoon, members of the Greek Orthodox Church held a reception in his honor, of which I was privileged to be chairperson.

He was very tired from travelling and exhausted from the afternoon performance, but his charm and interest in those who were waiting to welcome him left an everlasting memory. Now that more and more music lovers, musicians, collectors and historians are becoming aware of what this man's great talents really were, we can look forward to an even greater awareness by collectors and classical music buffs of the unique talent that continues to shine through every performance that has been left for us to enjoy again and again.

In essence, he was a model of the artistic integrity that made Ancient Greece so great. In fact, he felt proud of having been born into that Hellenic, and thus, Universal tradition. His devotion and ability to bring new "life" to the music he conducted, can never be denied. Undoubtedly, he was one of the great conductors of our time.

Nick Nickson
Rochester, New York
December, 1990

ΕΙΣΑΓΩΓΗ

Ένας περίπου αιώνας μας χωρίζει από την εποχή που κατασκευάστηκε ο πρώτος επίπεδος δίσκος γραμμοφώνου από τον Emile Berliner. Μεσα σ' αυτά τα εκατό χρόνια, η εξέλιξη της μεθόδου αναπαραγωγής του ήχου, από τους δίσκους 78 στροφών μέχρι τους δίσκους compact, είναι πραγματικά εντυπωσιακή. Η μεγάλη όμως σημασία της εφεύρεσης αυτής φαίνεται καθαρά ειδικά στην περίπτωση των μουσικών-εκτελεστών, αφού γι' αυτούς είναι ο μόνος τρόπος να διασωθεί το έργο τους και να γίνει προσιτό, για κρίση και μελέτη, στις επόμενες γενιές.

Για τον Δημήτρη Μητρόπουλο και την εντυπωσιακή σταδιοδρομία του έχουν γραφτεί αρκετά βιβλία και άρθρα που δίνουν μία ολοκληρωμένη εικόνα του καλλιτέχνη και του ανθρώπου. Όμως, επειδή οι κρίσεις που περιέχονται σ' αυτά ειναι εν πολλοίς υποκειμενικές, πιστεύω πως η τελική γνώμη του κάθε ακροατή θα πρέπει να διαμορφωθεί μόνο μετά από προσεκτική ακρόαση των ηχογραφήσεών του.

Σήμερα, τριάντα χρόνια μετά το θάνατό του και ενώ οι μνήμες, όσων τον είδαν και τον άκουσαν «διά ζώσης» να διευθύνει, αρχίζουν να ξεθωριάζουν, οι ηχογραφήσεις του αυτές παραμένουν ο μόνος ουσιαστικά τρόπος για την σωστή αξιολόγηση της προσφοράς του.

Η μοναδική σοβαρή προσπάθεια για μία δισκογραφία του Δ.Μ. έγινε το 1961 από τον Γ. Σ. Τσουγιόπουλο (βλ. Παράρτημα Α), όμως η εργασία αυτή παρουσιάζει κυρίως δύο σοβαρές ελλείψεις:
α) Παραλείπει αρκετές από τις εμπορικές ηχογραφήσεις του και όλες τις ακριβείς ημερομηνίες ηχογράφησης των δίσκων του και
β) Έχοντας γίνει πολλά χρόνια πριν και αμέσως μετά το θάνατό του δεν αναφέρει καμία από τις τόσο σημαντικές «ζωντανές» ηχογραφήσεις του, που τυπώθηκαν έκτοτε σε δίσκους.

Σκοπός αυτής της δισκογραφίας είναι όχι να υποδείξει τους δίσκους που πρέπει κανείς να αγοράσει, αλλά να καταγράψει κατά τον πληρέστερο δυνατό τρόπο τα υπάρχοντα ακροάματα βοηθώντας έτσι κάθε ενδιαφερόμενο να τα εντοπίσει και να τα μελετήσει, γιά να βγάλει μόνος τα τελικά συμπεράσματά του.

Με αυτά τα δεδομένα, ελπίζω πως η εργασία αυτή θα φανεί χρήσιμη σε κάθε ερευνητή, συλλέκτη ή απλό φιλόμουσο και θα συμπληρώσει, στο μέτρο του δυνατού, ένα σημαντικό κενό στη βιβλιογραφία του Δ.Μ.

Οι ηχογραφήσεις του Δ.Μ. σε δίσκους ειναι δύο ειδών:
1. Εμπορικές (Commercial). Ηχογραφήσεις, δηλαδή, που έγιναν σε studio ή κατά την διάρκεια συναυλιών του και τυπώθηκαν σε δίσκους απο τις εταιρείες με τις οποίες ο Δ.Μ. είχε υπογράψει συμβόλαιο. Σ' αυτές περιλαμβάνονται και οι λεγόμενες «ανέκδοτες» (unpublished) ηχογραφήσεις του, δηλαδή όσες από τις πιο πάνω για διαφόρους λόγους δεν έχουν ως σήμερα τυπωθεί σε δίσκους.
Οι Εμπορικές ηχογραφήσεις του Δ.Μ. έγιναν για τις εταιρείες Columbia και RCA Victor, με εξαίρεση τα λήμματα 1, 122 και 238 για την Cetra Soria, τα 167, 168 και 247 για την Decca USA και το 209 για την Counterpoint Esoteric. Τα 156, 176, 183, 253 και 273 της Metropolitan Opera Record Club ηχογραφήθηκαν απο την RCA Victor για λογαριασμό της ιδιωτικής λέσχης Book of the Month Club Inc.

2. Ζωντανές (Live). Ηχογραφήσεις, δηλαδή, που έγιναν παράνομα -συνήθως εν αγνοία του και χωρίς την έγκρισή του- κατά την διάρκεια είτε των συναυλιών του, είτε των ραδιοφωνικών αναμεταδόσεών τους. Οι ηχογραφήσεις αυτές έγιναν αρχικά σε πρότυπους δίσκους (acetates), ή σε μαγνητοταινίες και στη συνέχεια τυπώθηκαν σε δίσκους βινυλίου ή compact από διάφορες εταιρείες, μετά την πάροδο του χρόνου που απαιτείται για την παραγραφή των πνευματικών δικιωμάτων των εκτελεστών.

Η εργασία αυτή χωρίζεται στην κυρίως δισκογραφία και πέντε παραρτήματα,(Α ως Ε), που περιέχουν αντίστοιχα:
– Η κυρίως δισκογραφία περιέχει όλες τις ηχογραφήσεις του Δ.Μ σε δίσκους βινυλίου (78, 33, 45 στροφών) ή compact, με απόλυτη αλφαβητική σειρά του ονόματος του συνθέτη κάθε έργου. Όπου εκτελούνται περισσότερα του ενός έργα του ίδιου συνθέτη τότε αυτά αναγράφονται κατ' αλφαβητική σειρά έργου, και όπου το ίδιο έργο εκτελείται περισσότερες της μιάς φορές, τότε η καταγραφή γίνεται κατά τη χρονολογική σειρά που η κάθε εκτέλεση ηχογραφήθηκε.
Το κάθε λήμμα της δισκογραφίας αναφέρεται σε ένα μόνο ακρόαμα και περιέχει όλα τα βασικά στοιχεία για το έργο και την ηχογράφησή του, δηλαδή:
   α. Πλήρη περιγραφή του έργου.
   6. Τόπο και ακριβή ημερομηνία ηχογράφησης.
   γ. Ορχήστρα, χορωδία και σολίστες, όταν υπάρχουν.
   δ. Είδος, εταιρεία και αριθμό καταλόγου του δίσκου, για την πρώτη έκδοσή του και τις γνωστές ανατυπώσεις του.
Η ένδειξη (Live) κάτω απο τον τόπο εγγραφής δηλώνει οτι πρόκειται για ζωντανή ηχογράφηση, ενώ ένας αστερίσκος (*) μετά την περιγραφή του έργου παραπέμπει στο Παράρτημα Β όπου, με τον ίδιο αριθμό, υπάρχει σημείωση σχετική με αυτό το λήμμα.

INTRODUCTION

Almost one century has passed since the first flat gramophone record was made by Emil Berliner. During these hundred years, the technical evolution in sound reproduction, from the 78 rpm record to the compact disc, has been truly impressive. But the significance of this invention becomes much more apparent in the case of the musician-performer, since it is the only way that his work can survive and be passed on to future generations for evaluation and judgement.

Many books and articles have been written about the life and remarkable career of Dimitri Mitropoulos, which render an accurate picture of the artist and the man. However, because of the unavoidably subjective nature of the conclusions drawn, I believe that each listener's final verdict should only be reached after careful study of his recordings.

Today, thirty years from his death, and while the memories of those fortunate enough to have seen and heard him conduct in person begin to fade away, his contribution can only be fully appreciated through his records.

The only serious attempt at a Mitropoulos discography was made in 1961, by G. S. Tsougiopoulos. This compilation presents two serious drawbacks:
a) It omits some of his commercial recordings, and all the specific recording dates of the records listed and
b) being compiled so soon after his death, it understandably does not include many very important "Live" recordings of D.M. performances which have been issued on LP & CD since.

The aim of this discography is not to indicate or suggest the records which one should acquire, but to list all the existing recordings of D.M., thus assisting the listener to pinpoint and study them, in order to draw his own conclusions. So, in view of these facts, I hope that this work will be useful to music lovers, collectors and researchers alike, and will fill a gap in the bibliography of Mitropoulos.

The recordings of Mitropoulos can be divided in two broad categories:
1. Commercial recordings: Those made in the studio or during an actual performance, whether published or unpublished, by the record companies with which Mitropoulos had a contract. All of them were made for Columbia and RCA Victor, with the exception of entries 1, 122 and 238 which were made for Cetra Soria, entries 167, 168 and 247 for Decca USA, and entry 209 for Counterpoint Esoteric.
Entries 156, 176, 183, 253 and 273 of Metropolitan Opera Record Club, were recorded by RCA Victor for the Book of the Month Club Inc.

2. Pirate recordings: Those made illicitly by individuals or radio stations, without the Maestro's approval, during live performances or radio broadcasts of his concerts. They were originally recorded on acetates or tapes and more recently, when the statute of limitations on copyright law had expired, they were released by the various record companies in the LP or CD format. Here Mitropoulos conducts performances of some very important works by such composers as G.Mahler, W.A.Mozart, G.Verdi, G.Puccini, R.Strauss, R.Wagner et al. that have never been recorded commercially by him.
Here also the Maestro can be heard in his dual capacity of pianist - conductor, in works of Bach, Krenek and Prokofief, an endeavour that he particularly enjoyed and which greatly influenced his career.

The discography is divided into six parts, the main list and five Appendices (A to E) that comprise respectively:
– The main list contains all the recordings of D.M. that were issued on vinyl (78, LP, EP) or CD, in strict alphabetical order of the composer's name. Where more than one works by the same composer are present, they are also alphabetically placed, and where the same composition is performed more than once, chronological order of recording is observed. Each entry in the main list refers to only one performance of each work, and contains all the essential data on the composition and its recording i.e.
   a. Description of the composition
   b. Place and date of recording
   c. Orchestra, chorus and soloists, where applicable
   d. Type of record (78, LP, EP or CD), record company, catalogue number of the first edition and each known subsequent reprint.
The indication "Live" below the recording place, denotes a pirate recording, while an asterisk (*) following the description of the composition, refers to Appendix B, where there is a relevant note under the same number.

– Appendix A contains all the Greek and foreign sources that were used for this research.

Στο Παράρτημα Α περιέχονται όλες οι ελληνικές και ξένες πηγές που χρησιμοποιήθηκαν κατά τη διάρκεια τής έρευνας.

Στό Παράρτημα Β υπάρχουν σημειώσεις σχετικές με τα έργα ή τις μεταγραφές τους, τις ηχογραφήσεις ή τις εκτελέσεις τους. Η αρίθμηση τών σημειώσεων έγινε σύμφωνα με τον αριθμό που έχει το αντίστοιχο λήμμα στην κυρίως δισκογραφία.

Το Παράρτημα Γ είναι ένας συνοπτικός κατάλογος όλων των ηχογραφήσεων του Δ.Μ. που περιέχονται στην κυρίως δισκογραφία, με απόλυτη χρονολογική σειρά.

Το Παράρτημα Δ είναι το ευρετήριο ονομάτων όλων των καλλιτεχνών που συνεργάστηκαν με τον Δ.Μ., ή έπαιξαν υπό την διεύθυνσή του σε ηχογραφήσεις δίσκων.

Το Παράρτημα Ε περιλαμβάνει ηχογραφήσεις του Δ.Μ. που υπάρχουν σε μαγνητοταινίες, σε ιδιωτικά αρχεία ή ραδιοφωνικούς σταθμούς και δεν έχουν τυπωθεί μέχρι τώρα σε δίσκους οποιασδήποτε μορφής. Όλες οι ηχογραφήσεις αυτές είναι με την Φιλαρμονική της Νέας Υόρκης, εκτός αν σημειώνεται διαφορετικά, και έχουν καταχωρηθεί με χρονολογική σειρά.

Επειδή δεν μπορούμε να προσδιορίσουμε με ακρίβεια τί και πότε πρόκειται ακόμη να εκδοθεί ή να ανατυπωθεί σε δίσκους από τις εγγραφές αυτές, αποφασίσθηκε, σαν τελικό χρονικό όριο της εξαιρετικά επίπονης αυτής έρευνας που άρχισε το 1986, να ορισθεί η 1η Δεκεμβρίου του 1990 και έτσι η δισκογραφία αυτή περιέχει μόνον ότι κυκλοφόρησε μέχρι τότε.

Θα ήμουν ευγνώμων σε οποιονδήποτε μπορούσε να υποδείξει τυχόν παραλείψεις ή ανακρίβειες που θα ήταν δυνατόν να διορθωθούν σε επόμενη έκδοση αυτής της δισκογραφίας.

Στο σημείο αυτό αισθάνομαι την ανάγκη να ευχαριστήσω όλους όσους βοήθησαν να ολοκληρωθεί η εργασία αυτή και ιδιαίτερα τον αγαπητό μου φίλο Nick Nickson από το Rochester N.Y. ή Νίκο Νικητιάδη από τη Νίσσυρο, Διευθυντή Σχέσεων με την Κοινότητα του Ραδιοφωνικού σταθμού WHAM, πρώην διευθυντή του σταθμού κλασικής μουσικής WBFB-FM, παραγωγό τριών δίσκων, μέχρι στιγμής, με εκτελέσεις του Δ.Μ. που προέρχονται από σπανιότατους δίσκους 78 στροφών, ειδικό σε ότι αφορά τον Δ.Μ. και κάτοχο σχετικού αρχείου, επί πολλά χρόνια συλλέκτη και ερευνητή, που όχι μόνον βοήθησε, αλλά στάθηκε ένας πολύτιμος συνεργάτης σε όλες τις φάσεις της εργασίας αυτής η οποία χωρίς τη βοήθειά του δεν θα ήταν δυνατόν να πραγματοποιηθεί.

Τον Nathan E. Brown - υπεύθυνο του «Αμερικανικού Αρχείου Ηχογραφήσεων Κλασσικής Μουσικής», El Cerrito, CA. 94530

Τον Philip J. Conole - Διοικητικό Δ/ντή του Αρχείου "Frances R. Conole" - Πανεπιστήμιο της Πολιτείας της Νέας Υόρκης – στο Binghampton N.Y. 13901

Την Ελένη Γρηγορέα, τον Αλέξη Δ. Ζακυθηνό, το Μουσικολόγο-Καθηγητή Απόστολο Κώστιο,

τον Μουσικολόγο-Μουσικοκριτικό Γιώργο Λεωτσάκο, το Γιώργο Μανιάτη,

την Bernadette Moore - Διευθύντρια του Αρχείου της RCA Records, New York, N.Y. 10036,

τον Peter Munves - Διευθυντή του Masterworks Division της CBS Records Inc. New York, N.Y. 10019,

τον Τάσο Μωυσόγλου, τον Donald J. Ott - Κάτοχο σημαντικού αρχείου σχετικού με τον Δ.Μ. και συλλέκτη από το Scarsdale, New York, τον Γιάννη Πρεζάνη που επιμελήθηκε τα κείμενα,

τη Sallie Wood - Πρώην Διευθύντρια του Αρχείου της RCA Records, New York N.Y. 10036

την Πόπη Τσακιράκη της Εταιρείας ΗΡΙΝΝΑ – Ειδικές Εκδόσεις που ανέλαβε καί επιμελήθηκε την έκδοση αυτή.

Σήμερα, τριάντα χρόνια από το θάνατο του μέγιστου Έλληνα αρχιμουσικού, θα 'θελα η εργασία αυτή να θεωρηθεί ελάχιστη προσφορά στη μνήμη ενός ανθρώπου που ξόδεψε ολόκληρη τη ζωή του στην υπηρεσία της μουσικής. Ενός ανθρώπου ασκητικού, αφιλοκερδή και πάντα πρόθυμου να βοηθήση τους άλλους.

Ενός ανθρώπου που αγωνίστηκε για την καθιέρωση της σύγχρονης μουσικής και των συνθετών της, όσο κανένας άλλος αρχιμουσικός και του οποίου το σεμνό και ευγενικό χαρακτήρα δεν μπόρεσαν να αλλοιώσουν -όπως συνήθως συμβαίνει- οι μεγαλύτερες διακρίσεις και οι σημαντικότερες επιτυχίες.

Αθήνα, Δεκέμβριος 1990
Στάθης Α. Αρφάνης
Ρεθύμνου 8, 106 82 Αθήνα

Ενώ η εργασία αυτή βρισκόταν ήδη στο τυπογραφείο, το Υπουργείο Πολιτισμού αποφάσισε την μεταφορά σε δίσκους Compact των μαγνητοταινιών που ηχογραφήθηκαν από το Εθνικό Ίδρυμα Ραδιοφωνίας (τώρα ΕΡΑ) κατά την διάρκεια των συναυλιών του Δ.Μ. στην Αθήνα με την Φιλαρμονική της Νέας Υόρκης στις 1 και 2 Οκτωβρίου 1955 και που περιλαμβάνουν: την εισαγωγή από την "Forza del Destino" του G. Verdi, τις "Variations on a Theme by Haydn" του J. Brahms, τους Τέσσερις Ελληνικούς Χορούς του Ν. Σκαλκώτα, την «Ηρωϊκή» Συμφωνία του L. van Beethoven την 2η Συμφωνία του R. Schumann και την Συμφωνία αρ. 10 του D. Shostakovich. (6λ. Παράρτημα Ε). Παράλληλα η Ελληνική εταιρεία δίσκων Musica Viva ετοιμαζόταν να εκδόσει σε δίσκους βινυλίου και Compact την «Συμφωνία του Χριστού» του Χ. Περπέσα (6λ. Παράρτημα Ε). Δυστυχώς ως τώρα δεν έχουμε ακόμη τους αριθμούς των δίσκων αυτών και έτσι δεν μπορέσαμε να τους συμπεριλάβουμε στήν κυρίως δισκογραφία.

– In Appendix B, notes relevant to the compositions, their transcriptions, their recordings or their performances can be found.

– Appendix C is a list, in strict chronological order, of all the Mitropoulos recordings contained in the main list.

– Appendix D is the index of names of all the artists who collaborated with Mitropoulos in one way or another, or performed under his direction in recordings.

– Appendix E contains the known taped radio broadcasts of Mitropoulos' performances which can be found in private archives or radio stations and have not yet been transferred on records. Unless otherwise noted, all of them are with the New York Philharmonic Orchestra and are listed in chronological order. As this part of the research will be constantly updated, a deadline date has been determined and only the transfers known to the compiler by December 1st, 1990, are included.

I would be grateful to anyone who could point out any inaccuracies or omissions which will hopefully be corrected in a second edition of this discography.

At this point, I wish to thank all those who helped me with this work, and above all my dear friend Nick Nickson from Rochester, N.Y., alias Nicos Nikitiadis from Nisiros, Greece, Community Relations Manager of WHAM radio station, former director of WBFB-FM radio station, producer, so far, of three records (one LP & two CD's) that contain some of the rarest Mitropoulos 78 rpm records, a D.M. expert and archivist, a long-time collector and researcher, who has been an invaluable collaborator and without whose help this project would never have been completed.

Nathan E. Brown, Archivist of Classical Recordings Archive of America, El Cerrito, CA. 94530

Philip J. Conole, Executive director of "Frances R. Conole Archives", State University of New York, Binghampton, N.Y. 13901

Apostolos Costios, Professor-musicologist, Athens, Greece

Helena Grigorea, Athens, Greece

George Leotsakos, Musicologist-music critic, Athens, Greece

George Maniatis, Athens Greece

Bernadette Moore, Director of Archives, RCA Records, New York, N.Y. 10036

Peter Munves, Director of Masterworks Division, CBS Records Inc New York, N.Y. 10019

Tassos Moissoglou, Athens, Greece

Donald J. Ott, Collector and owner of a substantial private archive on Mitropoulos, Scarsdale, N.Y.

Yannis Prezanis, who edited the text

Sallie Wood, former Director of Archives, RCA Records, New York, N.Y. 10036

Alexis D. Zakythinos, Athens, Greece

and, finally, Popi Tsakiraki - IRINNA S.A. – Special editions, who undertook and supervised the publication of this book.

This work is meant as a tribute to the memory of a man who spent all his life serving music. An ascetic and disinterested man who was always eager to help others. A man who fought in the cause of contemporary music and its composers as no other conductor did and whose gentle and modest nature was never altered by success and distinctions.

Athens, December 1990
Stathis A. Arfanis.
8 Rethymnou st., 106 82 Athens, Greece

As we are going to press the Greek Ministry of Culture & Science decided to transfer on CD the existing tapes of Mitropoulos concerts with the New York Philharmonic of October 1 & 2 1955 at the Athens Festival, comprising the Overture from G. Verdi's "La Forza del Destino" J. Brahms "Variations on a Theme by Haydn", N. Skalkottas' "Four Greek Dances", L. van Beethoven's "Eroica", R. Schumann's Symphony no 2 and D. Shostakovich's Symphony no 10, while the Greek record company Musica Viva was about to issue on both vinyl and CD the H. Perpessas "Christus Symphony" (see Appendix E). Unfortunately the record numbers are unavailable to this date and these entries are not included in the main list of this dicography.

ABBREVIATIONS / ΣΥΝΤΟΜΟΓΡΑΦΙΕΣ

78	78 rpm record	Δίσκος 78 στροφών
AK	Apostolos Kostios (see sources)	Απόστολος Κώστιος (βλ. πηγές)
Arr.	Arrangement	Επεξεργασία
b	Baritone	Βαρύτονος
bs	Bass	Μπάσος
bs-b	Bass-Baritone	Μπάσο-Βαρύτονος
BWV	Bach Werke Verzeichnis	Κατάλογος έργων J. S. Bach
c	Contralto	Κοντράλτο
CD	Compact Disc	Δίσκος Compact
DM	Dimitri Mitropoulos	Δημήτρης Μητρόπουλος
EP	Extended Play (45 rpm record)	Ηυξημένης Διαρκείας (Δίσκος 45 στροφών)
KK	Katy Katsoyanni (see sources)	Καίτη Κατσογιάννη (βλ. πηγές)
KV	Köchel Verzeichnis	Κατάλογος Köchel (Για τα έργα του W. A. Mozart)
L	Live	Ζωντανή ηχογράφηση
LP	Long Play (33 rpm record)	Μακράς Διαρκείας (Δίσκος 33 στροφών)
ms	Mezzosoprano	Μεσόφωνος
Op.	Opus	Έργον
Orch.	Orchestration	Ενορχήστρωση
s	Soprano	Υψίφωνος
t	Tenor	Τενόρος
Trans.	Transcription	Μεταγραφή

ABBREVIATIONS OF ORCHESTRAS

BEJ & CMS	The Brass Ensemble of the Jazz & Classical Music Society
BPO	Berlin Philharmonic Orchestra
BRO	Bavarian Radio Orchestra
CAO	Concertgebouw Amsterdam Orchestra
CRO	Cologne Radio Orchestra
CSO	Columbia Symphony Orchestra
DSO	Detroit Symphony Orchestra
ISCM	International Society for Contemporary Music Concert Group
MMF	Maggio Musicale Fiorentino Festival Orchestra
MOO	Metropolitan Opera Orchestra
MSO	Minneapolis Symphony Orchestra
NBC	National Broadcasting Company Symphony Orchestra
NYPO	New York Philharmonic Orchestra
NYPSO	New York Philharmonic-Symphony Orchestra
	(In 1928 the New York Philharmonic & the New York Symphony Orchestra merged into one under the name of the New York Philharmonic-Symphony Orchestra. In the early fifties it was renamed as the New York Philharmonic Orchestra, although it retained its former name on the record sleeves until 28 February 1956).

NYPSW	New York Philharmonic Scholarship Winners Ensemble
RAI	Radiotelevisione Italiana Orchestra Torino
RCA	RCA Victor Symphony Orchestra
RHD	Robin Hood Dell Orchestra Philadelphia
TCF	Teatro Comunale di Firenze Orchestra
VPO	Vienna Philharmonic Orchestra

ABBREVIATIONS OF RECORD COMPANIES

AS Disc	Andrea Scarduelli Productions
CBS	Columbia Broadcasting System
Cab. Disc.	Cabaletta Discoreol
Cetra DOC	Fonit Cetra Documents
Cetra LO	Fonit Cetra Live Opera
CHROM	Chronicle of Music
CID	Compagnie Ind. du Disque
Columbia D	Columbia Demonstration Record
Columbia HL	Columbia Harmony
Columbia AAL, AL, BM, CL, ML, MS, SL.	Columbia Masterworks
Columbia PM	Columbia Promotion Recording
Columbia RL	Columbia Entré
Count-Esot	Counterpoint Esoteric
CRI	Composers Recordings Inc.
CSP	Columbia Special Products
GDS	Giuseppe di Stefano Records
GOP	Great Opera Performances
GUN-MAR	Gun-Mar (Gunther-Marie) Music Inc.
HMV	His Master's Voice
HOPE	Historical Opera Performances Edition
HUNT	Hunt Productions
MORC	Metropolitan Opera Record Club
Mov. Musica	Movimento Musica
MET	Metropolitan Opera Soria Series
NH Records	Nickson-Hill Records
NN Records	Nick Nickson Records
NWR	New World Records
NYP	New York Philharmonic / WQXR Radiothon Special Edition
OMR	Orion Master Recordings
OTARC	Off The Air Record Club
Ovation	Ovation Records (The Minnesota Orchestra's 75th Anniversary Collector's Set).
RCA	Radio Corporation of America
RDP	Readers' Digest Productions
RHR	Robin Hood Records
UORC	Unique Opera Record Company
Val. Records	Valentine Records - Longanesi Periodici
V-Disc	Victory Disc (Armed Forces Special Services Issue)

BACH, Johann Sebastian (1685-1750)

1. "Chaconne" from Partita for Solo Violin no 2 BWV 1004 *(Trans. A. Casella)* *

| Torino May 1950 | RAI | LP Cetra Soria LPC 50044 |
| | | CD NN Records NN 1003 |

2. Brandenburg Concerto no 5 in D major BWV 1050 *

| New York 16 Dec. 1945 | NBC | CD AS Disc AS 512 |
| (Live) | Dimitri Mitropoulos (piano) | |

3. Concerto for Harpsichord & Orchestra no 1 in d minor BWV 1052

   (Played in a transcription for Piano & Orchestra)

Salzburg 10 Aug. 1958	CAO	LP Discocorp IGI 206
(Live)	Glenn Gould (piano)	CD Nuova Era 013-6306
		CD Price-Less D 15119

4. Concerto for Three Harpsichords & Orchestra in d minor BWV 1063

   (Played in a transcription for three Pianos & Orchestra)

New York 27 Nov. 1950	NYPSO	LP Columbia ML 2196
	Robert,Gaby and Jean Casadesus	
	(pianos)	

5. Concerto for Violin & Orchestra in g minor BWV 1056

   (Trans. of Concerto for Harpsichord & Orchestra no 5 in f minor BWV 1056)

| New York 18 Dec. 1949 | NYPSO | LP Rococo 2037 |
| (Live) | Joseph Szigeti (violin) | LP Discocorp RR 532 |

6. Fantasia and Fugue for Organ in g minor BWV 542 *(Trans. D. Mitropoulos)* *

Minneapolis 6 Apr. 1942	MSO	78 Columbia 11993/94 D
		LP Ovation VM 5645
		CD NN Records NN-1002

7. Toccata Adagio and Fugue for Organ in C major BWV 564 *(Trans. L. Weiner)* *

| Minneapolis 3 & 4 Dec. 1940 | MSO | 78 Columbia 11528/29 D |
| | | CD NN Records NN-1002 |

8. "Wir glauben all'an einen Gott" Chorale Prelude for Organ BWV 680 *(Trans. H. Bösenroth)* *

   (from Lutheran Organ Mass BWV 669/89)

| Minneapolis 6 Apr. 1942 | MSO | 78 Columbia 11994 D |
| | | CD NN Records NN-1002 |

BARBER, Samuel (1910-1981)

9. "Vanessa" Opera in 4 Acts *(Complete)* *

(Libretto by Gian Carlo Menotti.
Premiere Recording)

New York 23 Feb. and 7 & 10 Apr. 1958			LP RCA LM/LSC 6138
	MOO & Chorus		LP RCA RL 02094 (2)
			CD RCA 7899-2-RG
	Asst. Conductor	: I. Strasfogel	CD RCA 87899
	Chorus Master	: K. Adler	*Excerpts*
			LP RCA LM/LSC 6062
	Vanessa	: E. Steber, s	LP RCA SP 33-21 (Act 1 A
	Erica	: R. Elias, ms	"Must the winter come so
	Baroness	: R. Resnik, c	soon ?" w. R. Elias)
	Anatol	: N. Gedda, t	LP RCA RL 85177 (8)
	Doctor	: G. Tozzi, bs	(Act 4 Quintet)
	Nicholas	: G. Cehanovsky, b	
	Footman	: R. Nagy, t	

10. "Medea's Meditation & Dance of Vengeance" Op. 23a

New York 16 Mar. 1958 (Live)	NYPO	CD AS Disc AS 543

BAX, Arnold Edward Trevor (1883-1953)

11. Overture to a Picaresque Comedy

New York 22 Apr. 1951 (Live)	NYPSO	LP OTARC OTA 8

BEETHOVEN, Ludvig van (1770-1827)

12. Concerto for Piano & Orchestra no 3 in c minor Op. 37
   (Recorded during actual performance)

New York 23 Feb. 1957	NYPO Jean Casadesus (piano)	LP CSP C 10954

13. Concerto for Piano & Orchestra no 4 in G major Op. 58

New York 22 Apr. 1951 (Live)	NYPSO Artur Rubinstein (piano)	LP OTARC OTA 8 CD AS Disc AS 532

14. Concerto for Piano & Orchestra no 5 in E flat major Op. 73 "Emperor"

Paris 19 Sep. 1955	NYPSO Robert Casadesus (piano)	LP Columbia ML 5100 LP CSP P 14201 LP Philips A 01.215 L

15. Concerto for Violin & Orchestra in D major Op. 61 *(Original Version)*

New York 15 Jan. 1950 (Live)	NYPSO Szymon Goldberg (violin)	LP Melodram MEL 210

16. Concerto for Violin & Orchestra in D major Op. 61 *

New York 26 Oct. 1952 (Live)	NYPSO Zino Francescatti (violin)	CD Melodram 18030

17. Concerto for Violin & Orchestra in D major Op. 61 *

New York 12 Feb. 1956 (Live)	NYPSO Jascha Heifetz (violin)	LP Melodram MEL 210 LP Movimento Musica 01.005 LP Arioso Historical 15.001

18. "Coriolan" Overture Op. 62

Minneapolis 10 Jan. 1940	MSO	78 Columbia 11175 D LP Columbia RL 3038

19. "Leonore" no 3 Overture Op. 72a

Minneapolis 10 Jan. 1940	MSO	78 Columbia 11288/89 D LP Columbia RL 3038

20. Mass in D major Op. 123 "Missa Solemnis"

New York 8 Nov. 1953 (Live)	NYPSO Westminster Choir Eleanor Steber, s Nell Tangeman, ms Harvey Smith-Spencer, t Mack Harrell, b	LP Melodram MEL 233

21. "The Creatures of Prometheus" Ballet Music Op. 43 *(Excerpts)*

New York 21 Feb. 1954 (Live)	NYPSO	CD AS Disc AS 532

22. Symphony no 1 in C major Op. 21 *

New York 31 Jan. 1954 (Live)	NYPSO	LP Melodram MEL 233 CD Melodram 18030 CD AS Disc AS 517

23. Symphony no 6 in F major Op. 68 "Pastoral"

Minneapolis 22 Jan. 1940	MSO	78 Columbia 11180/84 D LP Columbia RL 3009 LP Columbia HL 7120

24. Symphony no 8 in F major Op. 93

New York 5 May 1957 (Live)	NYPO	CD AS Disc AS 517

BERG, Alban (1885-1935)

25. Concerto for Violin & Orchestra "To the Memory of an Angel" *

New York 30 Dec. 1945 (Live)	NBC Joseph Szigeti (violin)	LP Discocorp WSA 701 LP Cetra DOC 3

26. "Wozzeck" Op. 7 Opera in 3 Acts, 15 Scenes *(Complete)*
(Libretto by the composer after Georg Büchner's drama. Recorded during actual performances. Premiere recording.)

New York 12,13 & 15 Apr. 1951	NYPSO High School of Music & Arts Chorus Schola Cantorum Chorus Chorus Master : H. Ross	LP Columbia SL 118 LP Columbia FCX 157/8 LP Odyssey Y2 33126 LP CBS M2P 42470 LP Philips ABL 3388 LP Philips A01.490/91L CD CBS 42470

Excerpts
LP Columbia BM 13
(Orchestral Interlude from Act 3)

Captain	: J. Mordino, t
Wozzeck	: M. Harrell, b
Andres	: D. Lloyd, t
Marie	: E. Farrell, s
Margret	: E. Eustis, c
Doctor	: R. Herbert, bs
Drum Major	: F. Jagel, t
Apprentice 1	: A. Anderson, bs
Apprentice 2	: H. Norville, b
Fool	: J. Mordino, t
Soldier	: J. Mordino, t
Marie's Child	: B. A. Herdt, s
Children	: High School of Music & Arts Chorus

BERLIOZ, Louis Hector (1803-1869)

27. "Les Nuits D' Été" Song Cycle Op. 7
Poèmes de Théophile Gautier
(Villanelle, Le spectre de la rose,
Sur les lagunes, Absence, Au cimetière,
L'Île inconnue.)

New York 21 Jan. 1954	CSO Eleanor Steber, s	LP Columbia ML 4940 LP Columbia ML 5843 LP Philips NBL 5029 LP Odyssey Y 32360 LP CBS 61430

28. "Requiem" (Grande Messe Des Morts) Op. 5

(Concert dedicated to the memory of Wilhelm Furtwängler
with a spoken introduction by Dimitri Mitropoulos)

| Salzburg 15 Aug. 1956 (Live) | VPO
Vienna State Opera Chorus
Leopold Simoneau, t | LP Cetra LO 509
LP Movimento Musica 02.024 |

29. "Requiem" (Grande Messe Des Morts) Op. 5

| Cologne 26 Aug. 1956 (Live) | CRO
Cologne Radio Chorus
Nicolai Gedda, t | CD HUNT 562 |

30. "Romeo and Juliet" Dramatic symphony Op. 17 *(Orchestral parts)*

(Introduction, Romeo's Reverie, Fête, Love Scene,
Queen Mab Scherzo, Death of Romeo.)

| New York 27 Oct. 1952 | NYPSO | LP Columbia ML 4632
LP Philips NBL 5028
LP CSP P 14177 |

31. "Symphonie Fantastique" Op. 14

| New York 24 Feb. 1957 | NYPO | LP Columbia ML 5188
LP Columbia MS 6030
LP Odyssey 32 16 0204
LP CBS 61465
LP CBS 73144
LP Philips SABL 108
LP Philips A 01.354 L
CD CBS MPK 45685 |

32. "Symphonie Fantastique" Op. 14

| Rochester 14 Apr. 1957 (Live) | NYPO | CD HUNT 562 |

BIZET, George (1838-1875)

33. "Carmen" Opera in 4 acts *(Complete)*

(Libretto by Henri Meilhac & Ludovic Halévy)

New York 12 Jan. 1957 (Live)	MOO & Chorus Chorus Master	: K. Adler	LP Cetra LO 48 LP Cetra DOC 45 LP HOPE 210
	Carmen	: R. Stevens, c	LP Paragon DSV 52002
	Micaela	: L. Amara, s	CD Nuova Era 2307/09
	Frasquita	: H. Krall, s	*Excerpts*
	Mercedes	: M. Roggero, ms	LP GDS 4001
	Don Jose	: M. del Monaco, t	LP Melodram MEL 675
	Escamillo	: F. Guarrera, b	
	Dancairo	: G. Cehanovsky, b	
	Rementado	: P. Franke, t	
	Zuniga	: N. Scott, bs	
	Morales	: C. Harvuot, b	

34. Symphony no 1 in C major

New York 25 Apr. 1954   NYPSO   CD AS Disc AS 617
(Live)

BLOCH, Ernest (1880-1959)

35. "Schelomo" Hebraic Rhapsody for Cello & Orchestra Op. 33

New York 21 Apr. 1951   NYPSO   LP Columbia ML 4425
                               Leonard Rose (cello)   LP CSP P 14167

BORODIN, Alexander Porfirevich (1833-1887)

36. "Polovtsian Dances" from Act 2 of the Opera Prince Igor
    (Chorus part omitted in this recording)

New York 1 Dec. 1952   NYPSO   LP Columbia CL 751
                                                       LP Columbia ML 4815
                                                       LP Philips NBL 5015
                                                       LP Philips A 01.227 L
                                                       LP Philips N 02.107 L
                                                       EP Columbia A 1823

37. "In the Steppes of Central Asia" Tone Picture

New York 20 Mar. 1953   NYPSO   LP Columbia CL 751
                                                       LP Columbia ML 4815
                                                       LP Philips NBL 5015
                                                       LP Philips A 01.227 L
                                                       LP Philips N 02.107 L

38. "In the Steppes of Central Asia" Tone Picture

New York 19 Apr. 1953   NYPSO   CD AS Disc AS 508
(Live)

39. Symphony no 2 in b minor "Bogatyr"

Minneapolis 7 Dec. 1941   MSO   78 Columbia 11902/5 D
                                                       CD NN Records NN 1003

40. Symphony no 2 in b minor "Bogatyr"

New York 2 Nov. 1953   NYPSO   LP Columbia ML 4966
                                                       LP CSP P 14195
                                                       LP Philips ABL 3079
                                                       LP Philips A 01.227 L

BRAHMS, Johannes (1833-1897)

41. "Academic Festival" Overture Op. 80

New York 9 Feb. 1958	NYPO	LP Cetra DOC 23
(Live)		LP NYP 87 1/2
		CD Melodram 18009

42. Concerto for Piano & Orchestra no 1 in d minor Op. 15

New York 12 Apr. 1953	NYPSO	CD Melodram 18009
(Live)	William Kapell (piano)	

43. Concerto for Piano & Orchestra no 1 in d minor Op. 15

New York 13 Feb. 1955	NYPSO	CD AS Disc AS 610
(Live)	Dame Myra Hess (piano)	

44. Concerto for Violin & Orchestra in D major Op. 77

New York 24 Oct. 1948	NYPSO	CD AS Disc AS 518
(Live)	Joseph Szigeti (violin)	

45. Concerto for Violin & Orchestra in D major Op. 77

Salzburg 24 Aug. 1958	VPO	LP Val. Records GCL 12
(Live)	Zino Francescatti (violin)	

46. Symphony no 3 in F major Op. 90

Florence 17 Jun. 1953	MMF	LP Cetra DOC 64
(Live)		

47. Symphony no 3 in F major Op. 90

New York 9 Feb. 1958	NYPO	LP Cetra DOC 23
(Live)		CD HUNT LSMH 34020
		Excerpts
		CD Melodram 18009
		Third Movement:
		Poco Allegretto

48. Symphony no 4 in e minor Op. 98

New York 28 Oct. 1956	NYPO	LP Cetra DOC 24
(Live)		CD HUNT LSMH 34020

49. Variations on a Theme by Haydn "St.Anthony's Choral" Op. 56a

Minneapolis 4 Apr. 1942	MSO	78 Columbia 11813/14 D
		LP Columbia RL 3038

50. Variations on a Theme by Haydn "St.Anthony's Choral" Op. 56a

New York 13 Feb. 1955	NYPSO	LP NYP 87 1/2
(Live)		

51. Variations on a Theme by Haydn "St. Anthony's Choral" Op. 56a

Seattle 8 May 1955 (Live)	NYPSO	CD AS Disc AS 610

BRUCH, Max (1838-1920)

52. Concerto for Violin & Orchestra no 1 in g minor Op. 26

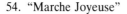

New York 4 Jan. 1952	NYPSO Zino Francescatti (violin)	LP Columbia ML 4575 LP Philips ABR 4011 LP Philips A 01.610

BUSONI, Ferruccio Benvenuto (1866-1924)

53. "Arlecchino" Theatrical Capriccio in 1 act *(Complete)*

(Text by the composer sung in English in a translation by Edward J. Dent. American Premiere Performance)

New York 14 Oct. 1951 (Live)	NYPSO	LP OTARC OTA 12

Sir Matteo	: W. Wilderman, b
Abate Cospicuo	: J. Pease, b
Dottor Bombasto	: J. Alden-Edkins, b
Arlecchino	: J. Brownlee, b
Leandro	: D. Lloyd, t
Colombina	: M. Lipton, c
Annunziata	: P. Polisi, s

CHABRIER, Alexis Emmanuel (1841-1894)

54. "Marche Joyeuse"

Minneapolis 7 Dec. 1941	MSO	78 Columbia 19013 D LP Columbia 3-201 LP NH Records NH 1001

CHARDON, Yves (1902-   )

55. "Rhumba" for Cello & Orchestra *

Minneapolis 2 Mar. 1945	MSO Yves Chardon (cello)	78 Columbia 13104 D CD NN Records NN 1002

CHAUSSON, Ernest (1855-1899)

56. Symphony in B flat major Op. 20

Minneapolis 9 Mar. 1946   MSO

78 Columbia 12955/58 D
LP Columbia ML 4141
LP CSP P 14149

57. Symphony in B flat major Op. 20

New York 26 Apr. 1953   NYPSO
(Live)

CD AS Disc AS 617

CHOPIN, Frédéric François (1810-1849)

58. "Chopiniana" *(Arr. Dimitri Rogal-Lewitzsky)* *
   *(Etude no 12 in c minor Op. 10, Nocturne no 13 in c minor Op. 48 no 1,
   Mazurka no 25 in b minor Op. 33 no 4, Valse no 14 Op. Posth.,
   Polonaise no 6 in A flat major Op. 53)*

Philadelphia 21 Sep. 1945   RHD

78 Columbia 12266/68 D

59. Concerto for Piano & Orchestra no 1 in e minor Op. 11

Minneapolis 6 Dec. 1941   MSO
                           Edward Kilenyi (piano)

78 Columbia 11840/43 D
LP Columbia RL 3028

CIMAROSA, Domenico (1749-1801)

60. "Beautiful Grecian" Overture

New York 21 Feb. 1954   NYPSO
(Live)

CD AS Disc AS 539

COPLAND, Aaron (1900-1990)

61. "Appalachian Spring" Suite

New York 7 Feb. 1954   NYPSO
(Live)

CD AS Disc AS 543

COUPERIN, François "Le Grand" (1668-1733)

62. Overture & Allegro from Sonata "La Sultane" *(Arr. Darius Milhaud)*

Minneapolis 2 Mar. 1945   MSO

78 Columbia 12161 D
CD NN Records NN 1002

63. Overture & Allegro from Sonata "La Sultane" *(Arr. Darius Milhaud)*

New York 4 Jan. 1952　　　NYPSO　　　　　　　　　　　　LP Columbia AAL 16

DEBUSSY, Claude Achille (1862-1918)

64. "Iberia" no 2 from "Images" pour Orchestre

New York 7 Feb. 1954　　　NYPSO　　　　　　　　　　　CD AS Disc AS 617
(Live)

65. "La Mer" Three Symphonic Sketches

New York 27 Nov. 1950　　NYPSO　　　　　　　　　　　LP Columbia ML 4344
　　　　　　　　　　　　　　　　　　　　LP Philips　A 01100 L
　　　　　　　　　　　　　　　　　　　　　　　　　　　　LP Philips　06683
　　　　　　　　　　　　　　　　　　　　　　　　　　　　LP CSP　P 14168

DUKAS, Paul (1865-1935)

66. "The Sorcerer's Apprentice" Scherzo for Orchestra

Minneapolis 3 Dec. 1940　　MSO　　　　　　　　　　　78 Columbia 11671/72 D
　　　　　　　　　　　　　　　　　　　　　　　　　　　　LP Columbia RL 3021
　　　　　　　　　　　　　　　　　　　　　　　　　　　　LP Columbia HL 7129

67. "The Sorcerer's Apprentice" Scherzo for Orchestra

New York 2 Nov. 1956　　　NYPO　　　　　　　　　　　LP Columbia ML 5198

DVORÁK, Antonin (1841-1904)

68. Slavonic Dances Op. 46 nos 1 & 3

Minneapolis 3 Dec. 1940　　MSO　　　　　　　　　　　78 Columbia 11645 D
　　　　　　　　　　　　　　　　　　　　　　　　　　　　LP Columbia HL 7129
　　　　　　　　　　　　　　　　　　　　　　　　　　　　LP Ovation　VM 5645
　　　　　　　　　　　　　　　　　　　　　　　　　　　　　(Op. 46 no 3 only)

69. Concerto for Cello & Orchestra in b minor Op. 104

Minneapolis 4 Apr. 1942　　MSO　　　　　　　　　　　Columbia UNPUBLISHED
　　　　　　　　　　　　　　Gregor Piatigorsky (cello)

70. Concerto for Violin & Orchestra in a minor Op. 53

New York 4 Mar. 1951　　　NYPSO　　　　　　　　　　LP Mov. Musica 01.068
(Live)　　　　　　　　　　Isaak Stern (violin)　　　　　CD Mov. Musica 011.006

FALLA, Manuel de (1876-1946)

71. Three Dances from The Ballet "The Three Cornered Hat"
(The Neighbors, The Miller's Dance, Final Dance.)

New York 2 Nov. 1953	NYPSO	LP Columbia ML 5172
		LP Columbia AL 44
		LP CBS BLD 7098
		EP Philips 400.010

72. Interlude & Dance from Act 1 of the Opera "La Vida Breve"

New York 2 Nov. 1953	NYPSO	LP Columbia ML 5172
		LP Columbia AL 44
		LP CBS BLD 7098

73. "Nights in the Gardens of Spain" for Piano & Orchestra

New York 2 Nov. 1956 &	NYPO	LP Columbia ML 5172
	Robert Casadesus (piano)	LP CBS BLD 7098
21 Mar. 1957	Harpist of the New York	LP Philips L 01.361 L
(Harp Dubbing only)	Philharmonic (Name unknown)	

FRANCK, César Auguste (1822-1890)

74. Symphonic Variations for Piano & Orchestra

New York 19 Apr. 1953	NYPSO	CD AS Disc AS 508
(Live)	Artur Rubinstein (piano)	

75. Symphony in d minor

Minneapolis 8 Jan. 1940	MSO	78 Columbia 11462/66 D
(Partial remake 26 Nov.1940)		LP Columbia RL 3006
		LP Columbia HL 7102

GINASTERA, Alberto (1916-1983)

76. Overture to the "Creole Faust"

New York 24 Feb. 1957	NYPO	CD AS Disc AS 543
(Live)		

GLAZUNOV, Alexander Konstantinovich (1865-1936)

77. Overture on Three Greek Themes Op. 3 no 1

Minneapolis 6 Apr. 1942	MSO	78 Columbia 11871/72 D
		LP NH Records NH 1001
		CD NN Records NN 1002

GLIÈRE, Reinhold Moritzovich (1875-1956)

78. "Sailor's Dance" from Act 1 of the Ballet "The Red Poppy"

Minneapolis 7 Dec. 1941   MSO

78 Columbia 11905 D
78 Columbia 12899 D
LP Columbia RL 3021
LP Columbia HL 7129

GLINKA, Mikhail Ivanovitch (1804-1857)

79. "Russlan & Ludmilla" Overture

New York 26 Feb. 1956   NYPSO
(Live)

CD AS Disc AS 502

GOULD, Morton (1913-   )

80. "Fall River Legend" Ballet Suite

New York 31 Mar. 1952   NYPSO

LP Columbia ML 4616
LP NWR NW 253

81. "Philharmonic Waltzes" *
*(Written for New York Philharmonic Orchestra's 1948
Annual Ball & Pension Fund Concert. Premiere Recording)*

New York 23 Jan. 1950   NYPSO

78 Columbia 13139 D
LP Columbia ML 2167
LP Columbia BM 39

82. "Minstrel Show"

Minneapolis 20 Jan. 1947   MSO

78 RCA 11-9654
LP NH Records NH 1001

GRIEG, Edvard Hagerup (1843-1907)

83. "Two Elegiac Melodies" Op. 34
(Heart Wounds, The Last Spring)

Minneapolis 3 Dec. 1940   MSO

78 Columbia 11698 D
CD NN Records NN 1002

Columbia Masterworks' advertisements of the first D. Mitropoulos 78 rpm records.

(coll. Nick Nickson)

Columbia Masterworks

Supplement for February, 1941

DIMITRI MITROPOULOS
conducts THE MINNEAPOLIS
SYMPHONY ORCHESTRA
in a superb new record
of César Franck's immo
SYMPHONY IN D MI
Set—M—AM—MM—

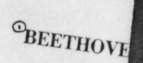

DIMITRI MITROP

○ BEETHOV

MINNEAPOLIS SY
DIMITRI MITROP

With this magnificent performance of Beethoven's "Pastorale" by the Minne
phony Orchestra, conducted by Dimitri Mitropoulos, Columbia is happy to ann
its great American orchestral series is now full under way.
Long a great favorite with the public, the Pastorale appeals both to the analytic
and to the lover of tuneful, effervescent music. The movements have been given d
titles—"The awakening of joyful feelings on arriving in the country", "By th
"Rejoicing of the peasants", "The storm" and "Gladsome and thankful feelings
storm"—probably as an afterthought to accompany the score's pastoral mood.
The tonal magnificence of the Minneapolis Symphony Orchestra and the acute pe
of its inspiring conductor, achieve an artistic excellence matched only by the sple
the Columbia recording.

Complete with Album
Price **$10.00**

Five 12-Inch Records—Set M-401 (11180-D—11
Automatic Couplings—Set AM-401 (11185-D—11

○ **BEETHOVEN: CORIOLAN OVERTURE, OP. 62**
MINNEAPOLIS SYMPHONY ORCHESTRA
DIMITRI MITROPOULOS, Conductor

As a prelude to its feature release next month, the Minneapolis Symphony Orchestra, conducted by Dimitri Mitropoulos, pro-
vides an exciting and dramatic
performance of Beethoven's overture based on Shakespeare's trag-
edy, "Coriolanus." This powerful
music is a splendid vehicle for
revealing the glowing tone of the
Minneapolis Orchestra and the
interpretative powers of its amaz-
ing conductor, Dimitri Mitropoulos. The brilliant recording of
overture truly heralds a great series to be
t month with the release of one of the
s in the orchestral repertoire.

12-Inch Record (11175-D)

NEW COLUMBIA
MASTERWORKS FOR APRIL

Dimitri Mitropoulos . . . famed
conductor of The Minneapolis Symphony
Orchestra which this month plays Beethoven's
"Pastorale" on Columbia Masterworks.

(Complete listing of Columbia Masterworks released since
Nov., and Brunswick Standard Records since Sept., 1939)

DIMITRI
MITROPOULOS
reviews
COLUMBIA MASTERWORKS
for JUNE, 1941

GREATEST RELEASE IN COLUMBIA'S HISTORY!

GUARNIERI, Camargo (1907-   )

84. Prologo y Fuga

New York 16 Mar. 1958   NYPO   CD AS Disc AS 543
(Live)

HÄNDEL, Georg Friedrich (1685-1759)

85. "Largo" from the Opera "Xerxes" *(Orch. B. Molinari)* *

Minneapolis 6 Apr. 1942   MSO   Columbia UNPUBLISHED

HAYDN, Franz Joseph (1732-1809)

86. English Opera Overture

New York 7 Feb. 1954   NYPSO   CD AS Disc AS 539
(Live)

87. Symphony no 80 in d minor

New York 7 Feb. 1954   NYPSO   CD AS Disc AS 539
(Live)

88. Symphony no 100 in G major "Military"

New York 4 Nov. 1956   NYPO   CD AS Disc AS 539
(Live)

HINDEMITH, Paul (1895-1963)

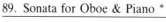

89. Sonata for Oboe & Piano *

New York 21 Apr. 1952   Harold Gomberg   (oboe)   LP Columbia ML 5603
                             Dimitri Mitropoulos (piano)

90. "The Harmony of the World" Symphony

New York 25 Oct. 1953   NYPSO   CD AS Disc AS 540
(Live)

IPPOLITOV-IVANOV, Mikhail Mikhailovich
(1859-1953)

91. "Caucasian Sketches" Op. 10 Suite

New York 20 Mar. 1953	NYPSO	LP Columbia CL 751
		LP Columbia ML 4815
		LP Philips NBL 5015
		LP Philips N 02.107 L
		LP Philips S 06 626
		EP Columbia A 1824

KEY, Francis Scott (1779-1843)

92. "The Star Spangled Banner" American National Anthem
   (Based on melody of old English drinking song
   "To Anacreon in Heaven" by John Stafford Smith)

| New York 11 Nov. 1957 | NYPO | Columbia UNPUBLISHED |

KHACHATURIAN, Aram Ilich (1903-1978)

93. Concerto for Piano & Orchestra in D flat major

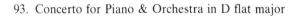

New York 3 Jan. 1950	NYPSO	78 Columbia 13075/79 D
	Oscar Levant (piano)	LP Columbia ML 4288
		LP Columbia FCX 136
		LP CSP P 14162

KIRCHNER, Leon (1919-   )

94. Concerto for Piano & Orchestra *
   Commissioned by the Koussevitzky Foundation.
   Recorded under the auspices of the Walter W. Naumburg Foundation.
   (Premiere Recording)

New York 24 Feb. 1956	NYPSO	LP Columbia ML 5185
	Leon Kirchner (piano)	LP CSP CML 5185
		LP NWR NW 286

KODÁLY, Zoltán (1882-1967)

95. Dances from Galanta

| New York 25 Jan. 1954 | NYPSO | Columbia UNPUBLISHED |

96. "Hary Janos" Suite from the Opera

| New York 27 Feb. 1956 | NYPSO | LP Columbia ML 5101 |
| | | LP CSP P 14202 |

KRENEK, Ernst (1900-   )

97. Concerto for Piano & Orchestra no 3 Op. 107 *

New York 11 Dec. 1949 (Live)	NYPSO Dimitri Mitropoulos (piano)	CD AS Disc AS 512

98. "Symphonic Elegy" for String Orchestra (In Memoriam Anton von Webern) *

New York 21 Apr. 1951	NYPSO	LP Columbia ML 4524 LP Philips ABL 3393

LALO, Victor Antoine Edouard (1823-1892)

99. "Le Roi d'Ys" Overture from the Opera

Minneapolis 2 Mar. 1945	MSO	78 Columbia 13104/05 D LP Columbia ML 2123 LP Columbia HL 7129

100. "Symphonie Espagnole" in d minor Op. 21 for Violin & Orchestra
(Third Movement "Intermezzo, Allegretto non troppo"
omitted in this recording)

New York 22 Apr. 1957	NYPO Zino Francescatti (violin)	LP Columbia ML 5184 LP Columbia ML 5601 LP Columbia MS 6201 LP CBS MP 38761 LP CBS 60262 LP Odyssey Y 33229 LP Philips ABL 3296 LP Philips L01.361L *Excerpts* (Second Movement: Scherzando, Allegro molt LP Columbia ML 5693 LP Columbia MS 6293 LP Columbia PM 1,PMS 1

LEONCAVALLO, Ruggero (1857-1919)

101. "I Pagliacci" Opera in a Prologue & 2 Acts (Highlights)
(Libretto by the composer)

New York 3 Jan. 1959 (Live)	MOO & Chorus	LP Val. Records GML 11 LP Foyer 1035
	Nedda : L. Amara, s	LP Joker SM 1299
	Canio : M. del Monaco, t	
	Tonio : L. Warren, b	
	Silvio : M. Sereni, b	
	Beppe : C. Anthony, t	

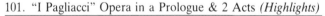

LISZT, Franz (1811-1886)

102. Concerto for Piano & Orchestra no 1 in E flat major

Florence 17 Jun. 1953 (Live)	MMF Arturo Benedetti-Michelangeli (piano)	LP Cetra DOC 64

103. "Les Préludes" Symphonic Poem no 3

New York 24 Feb. 1956	NYPSO	Columbia UNPUBLISHED

104. "Les Préludes" Symphonic Poem no 3

New York 27 Feb. 1956	NYPSO	LP Columbia ML 5198

105. "Rhapsodie Espagnole" for Piano & Orchestra *(Arr. Ferruccio Busoni)* *

Minneapolis 10 Jan. 1940	MSO Egon Petri (piano)	78 Columbia 11202/03 D LP Columbia RL 3040 CD Pearl GEMM 9347 CD NN Records NN 1003

LÖFFLER, Charles Martin (1861-1935)

106. Two Rhapsodies for Oboe, Viola & Piano *

New York 21 Apr. 1952	Harold Gomberg (oboe) Milton Katims (viola) Dimitri Mitropoulos (piano)	LP Columbia ML 5603

LULLY, Jean Baptiste (1632-1687)

107. Menuet from "Le Temple de la Paix" Ballet Suite *(Arr. Felix Mottl)* *

Minneapolis 3 Dec. 1940	MSO	78 Columbia 11566 D 78 Columbia 12900 D LP NH Records NH 1001

MAHLER, Gustav (1860-1911)

108. Symphony no 1 in D major "Titan"
    (Premiere Recording)

Minneapolis 4 Nov. 1940	MSO	78 Columbia 11609/14 D LP Columbia ML 4251 LP Columbia RL 3120 LP Columbia 33 CX 1068 LP CSP P 14157

109. Symphony no 1 in D major "Titan"

New York 21 Oct. 1951   NYPSO   LP Cetra LO 514
(Live)

110. Symphony no 1 in D major "Titan"

New York 15 Jun. 1955   NYPSO   LP Val. Records GCL 20
(Live)

111. Symphony no 1 in D major "Titan" *

New York 9 Jan. 1960   NYPO   LP Cetra DOC 43
(Live)   CD HUNT 556

112. Symphony no 3 in d minor

New York 15 Apr. 1956   NYPO   LP Cetra LO 514
(Live)   Westminster Chorus   LP Cetra DOC 43
                             Beatrice Krebs, c   CD HUNT 557

113. Symphony no 3 in d minor *

Cologne 31 Oct. 1960   CRO   LP Rococo 2055
(Live)   Cologne Radio Women's Chorus   LP Cetra DOC 4
                             Cologne School Boys' Chorus   LP Mov. Musica 02.016
                           Lucretia West, c

114. Symphony no 5 in c sharp minor

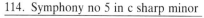

New York 28 May 1955   NYPSO   LP Mov. Musica 02.005
(Live)

115. Symphony no 5 in c sharp minor *

New York 2 Jan. 1960   NYPO   LP Replica ARPL 32463
(Live)   LP Cetra DOC 43
                                            LP NYP 88 1/2
                                            CD HUNT 523

116. Symphony no 6 in a minor "Tragic" *

New York 10 Apr. 1955   NYPSO   LP Replica ARPL 32463
(Live)   LP Cetra DOC 43

117. Symphony no 6 in a minor "Tragic"

(Concert to commemorate the 100th anniversary of G. Mahler's birth)

Cologne 31 Aug. 1959   CRO   LP Cetra DOC 5
(Live)   LP Mov. Musica 02.015
                                            CD HUNT 522

ΩΔΕΙΟΝ ΑΘΗΝΩΝ

Front page of the Athens Odeon Orchestra's programmes during the thirties.
Painting by N. Gysis. (coll. S.A. Arfanis)

118. Symphony no 8 in E flat major "Symphony of a Thousand"

Salzburg 28 Aug. 1960	VPO	LP Everest 3189/2
		LP Everest 3441
(Live)	Chorus of the Friends of Music	LP Ars Nova C 25/125
	Vienna State Opera Chorus	LP Sine Qua Non SQN 118
	Vienna Boys' Chorus	CD HUNT 558
	Magna Peccatrix : M. Cörtse, s	
	Mater Gloriosa : H. Zadek, s	
	Una Poenitentium : H. Zadek, s	
	Mulier Samaritana : L. West, c	
	Maria Aegyptiaca : I. Malaniuk, c	
	Doctor Marianus : G. Zampieri, t	
	Pater Ecstaticus : H. Prey, b	
	Pater Profundus : O. Edelmann, bs-b	

119. Symphony no 9 in D major *

New York 23 Jan. 1960	NYPO	LP Replica RPL 2460/61
(Live)		LP Cetra DOC 43
		LP Mov. Musica 02.026
		CD HUNT 521

120. Symphony no 10 in F sharp major : Adagio

| New York 15 Jun. 1955 | NYPSO | LP Mov. Musica 02.005 |
| (Live) | | |

121. Symphony no 10 in F sharp major : Adagio *

New York 16 Jan. 1960	NYPO	LP Replica RPL 2460/61
(Live)		LP Cetra DOC 43
		CD HUNT 556

MALIPIERO, Gian Francesco (1882-1973)

122. Symphony no 7 "Delle Canzoni"
(Premiere Recording)

| Torino May 1950 | RAI | LP Cetra Soria LPC 50044 |

MASCAGNI, Pietro (1863-1945)

123. "Intermezzo" from Act 2 of the Opera "Cavalleria Rusticana"

Philadelphia 26 Jul. 1946	RHD	78 Columbia 12982 D
		LP Columbia ML 2053
		EP Columbia AL 1637

124. "Addio alla Madre" Turridu's Aria from Act 2 of the Opera "Cavalleria Rusticana"

Detroit 7 Oct. 1945	DSO	78 V-Disc 623-B
(Live)	(Under the pseudonym of	CD NN Records NN 1003
	Ford Symphony Orchestra)	
	Jussi Björling, t	

MASSENET, Jules Emile Frederic (1842-1912)

125. "Scènes Alsaciennes" Suite for Orchestra Op. 7

Minneapolis 11 Mar. 1946	MSO	78 Columbia 12710/12 D
		LP Columbia ML 2074

126. "Meditation" from Act 2 of the Opera "Thais"

Minneapolis 6 Apr. 1942	MSO Violinist of the Minneapolis Symphony (Name unknown)	Columbia UNPUBLISHED

MENDELSSOHN-BARTHOLDY, Felix (1809-1847)

127. "Calm Sea and Prosperous Voyage" Overture Op. 27

New York 2 Nov. 1953	NYPSO	Columbia UNPUBLISHED

128. "Capriccio Brillant" for Piano & Orchestra Op. 22

Minneapolis 4 Dec. 1940	MSO Joanna Graudan (piano)	78 Columbia 11565/66 D LP Columbia ML 4127 CD NN Records NN 1003

129. Concerto for Violin & Orchestra in e minor Op. 64

New York 17 Nov. 1954	NYPSO
	Zino Francescatti (violin)
		LP Columbia ML 4965
		LP Columbia A -1109
		LP Philips ABL 3159
		LP Philips A 01.214
		LP CBS Sonny 20 AC 1900
		Excerpts
		LP Columbia D 2
		    Third Movement:
		    Allegretto non troppo

130. "Hebrides" (Fignal's Cave) Overture Op. 26

New York 2 Nov. 1953	NYPSO	LP Columbia AL 52

131. "Scherzo" from Octet in E flat major for strings Op. 20 *(Orch. F. Mendelssohn)*

Minneapolis 10 Jan. 1940	MSO	78 Columbia 11239 D 78 Columbia 12900 D LP NH Records NH 1001

132. "Ruy Blas" Overture Op. 95

New York 2 Nov. 1953	NYPSO	LP Columbia AL 52 LP Columbia A-1923

133. Symphony no 3 in a minor Op. 56 "Scotch"

| Minneapolis 6 Dec. 1941 | MSO | 78 Columbia 11968/71 D |
| | | LP Columbia RL 3017 |

134. Symphony no 3 in a minor Op. 56 "Scotch"

New York 2 Nov. 1953	NYPSO	LP Columbia ML 4864
		LP CSP P 14189
		LP Philips GBL 5550
		LP Philips ABL 3082
		LP Philips A 01.174 L
		Excerpts
		LP Columbia ML 5227
		Third Movement: Adagio

135. Symphony no 3 in a minor Op. 56 "Scotch" *

| Cologne 24 Oct. 1960 | CRO | LP Val. Records GCL 33 |
| (Live) | | CD Virtuoso 2697032 |

136. Symphony no 5 in d minor Op. 107 "Reformation"

New York 2 Nov. 1953	NYPSO	LP Columbia ML 4864
		LP CSP P 14189
		LP Philips GBL 5550
		LP Philips ABL 3082
		LP Philips A 01.174 L
		Excerpts
		LP Columbia ML 5227
		Third Movement: Andant

137. Symphony no 5 in d minor Op. 107 "Reformation"

| Cologne 19 Jul. 1957 | CRO | LP Mov. Musica 01.031 |
| (Live) | | LP Arioso Historical 15.006 |

MENNIN, Peter (1923-1983)

138. Symphony no 3
   (Recorded under the auspices of the Walter W. Naumburg Foundation)

| New York 1 Feb. 1954 | NYPSO | LP Columbia ML 4902 |
| | | LP CRI SD 278 |

MENOTTI, Gian Carlo (1911-   )

139. "Sebastian" Ballet Suite
   (Record sponsored by Ballet Associates in America Inc.)

| Philadelphia 26 Jul. 1946 | RHD | 78 Columbia 12573/74 D |
| | | LP Columbia ML 2053 |

MEYERBEER, Giacomo (1791-1864)

140. "Coronation March" from Act 3 of the Opera "Le Prophète"

Minneapolis 7 Dec. 1941	MSO	78 Columbia 19013 D LP Columbia 3-201 LP Columbia HL 7129

MILHAUD, Darius (1892-1974)

141. "Le Bœuf sur le Toit" Ballet

Minneapolis 2 Mar. 1945	MSO	78 Columbia 12932/33 D LP Columbia ML 2032

MOZART, Wolfgang Amadeus (1756-1791)

142. Concerto for Piano & Orchestra no 16 in D major KV 451

New York 23 Oct. 1955 (Live)	NYPSO Rudolf Serkin (piano)	LP Mov. Musica 01.007 CD HUNT LSMH 34008 CD AS Disc AS 511

143. Concerto for Piano & Orchestra no 20 in d minor KV 466

Florence 17 Jun. 1953 (Live)	MMF Arturo Benedetti-Michelangeli (piano)	LP Cetra DOC 64 CD HUNT 552

144. Concerto for Piano & Orchestra no 25 in C major KV 503

New York 23 Oct. 1955 (Live)	NYPSO Rudolf Serkin (piano)	LP Mov. Musica 01.007 CD HUNT LSMH 34008 CD AS Disc AS 511

145. Concerto for Two Pianos & Orchestra no 10 in E flat major KV 365

Philadelphia 21 Sep. 1945	RHD Vitya Vronsky & Victor Babin (pianos)	78 Columbia 12389/91 D LP Columbia ML 4098

146. Concerto for Two Pianos & Orchestra no 10 in E flat major KV 365

New York 13 Nov. 1955 (Live)	NYPSO Robert & Gaby Casadesus (pianos)	CD AS Disc AS 544

147. Concerto for Violin & Orchestra no 3 in G major KV 216

New York 18 Dec. 1949 (Live)	NYPSO Joseph Szigeti (violin)	LP Discocorp RR 532 CD AS Disc AS 518

THEATRE NATIONAL

CONCERT DE GALA

DONNÉ EN L'HONNEUR DES DÉLEGUÉS

DU XXVIIᵉ CONGRÈS DE LA PAIX

ORCHESTRE SYMPHONIQUE
DES INSTITUTS MUSICAUX
D'ATHÈNES

SOUS LA DIRECTION

DE M. D. MITROPOULO

COMPOSITEUR ET CHEF D'ORCHESTRE

AVEC LE GRACIEUX CONCOURS

DE Mᵐᵉ MARICA
PHOCAS - CALFOPOULO

(DU CONSERVATOIRE NATIONAL)

ET DE

M. PIERRE EPITROPAKIS

(DE L'OPÉRA GREC)

Le Mardi 8 Octobre
à 9ʰˢ ³/₄ heures du soir
très précises.

1925

IMPR. "HESTIA" 4462

PAX ET PLUTUS

Programme of the Gala concert given at the National Theatre, Athens, in 1925, in honour of the delegates of the 27th Peace Congress.
(coll. S.A. Arfanis)

148. Concerto for Violin & Orchestra no 5 in A major KV 219 "Turkish"

(D. Oistrakh's debut performance in America)

New York 1 Jan. 1956	NYPSO	CD HUNT LSMH 34018
(Live)	David Oistrakh (violin)	CD AS Disc AS 502

149. "Don Giovanni" Drama Giocoso in 2 Acts KV 527 *(Complete)* *

(Libretto by Lorenzo da Ponte)

Salzburg 24 Jul. 1956	VPO	LP Replica ARPL 42.422
(Live)	Vienna State Opera Chorus	LP Cab. Disc. DR 10021/23
		CD HUNT 552

Don Giovanni	: C. Siepi, bs
Donna Anna	: E. Grümmer, s
Donna Elvira	: L. della Casa, s
Zerlina	: R. Streich, s
Commendatore	: G. Frick, bs
Ottavio	: L. Simoneau, t
Leporello	: F. Corena, bs
Masetto	: W. Berry, b

150. "Idomeneo Re di Creta" Overture KV 366 *(Arr. F. Busoni)* *

New York 28 Dec. 1941	NYPSO	CD AS Disc AS 502
(Live)		

151. "Magic Flute" Overture KV 620

New York 9 Dec. 1945	NBC	CD HUNT 552
(Live)		

152. "Magic Flute" Overture KV 620

New York 2 Feb. 1958	NYPO	CD AS Disc AS 502
(Live)		CD AS Disc AS 544

153. "Le nozze di Figaro" Overture KV 492

New York 12 Apr. 1953	NYPSO	CD AS Disc AS 502
(Live)		

154. Symphony no 39 in E flat major KV 543

New York 22 Apr. 1951	NYPSO	LP OTARC OTA 8
(Live)		CD AS Disc AS 544

155. Entr'Actes 1 & 2 from "Thamos King of Egypt" KV 345

Minneapolis 3 Dec.1940	MSO	78 Columbia 11578 D
		LP NH Records NH 1001

MUSSORGSKY, Modest Petrovich (1839-1881)

156. "Boris Godounov" Opera in 4 Acts with a Prologue *(Abridged)*

(Libretto by the composer after A. Puschkin's play.
Revised & edited by Karol Rathaus.
Sung in English Text by John Gutman)
Recorded for the "Book of the Month Club Inc".

New York Mar. 1956	MOO & Chorus		LP MORC MO 417
	Asst. Conductor	: I. Strasfogel	LP RCA LM 6063 (Without
	Chorus Master	: K. Adler	Narration)
	Narrator	: C. Kullman	
	Boris	: G. Tozzi, bs	
	Marina	: N. Rankin, c	
	Shuiski	: C. Kullman, t	
	Dimitri	: A. da Costa, t	
	Pimen	: N. Scott, bs	
	Simpleton	: P. Franke, t	
	Rangoni	: F. Valentino, b	
	Fyodor	: M. Roggero, ms	
	Xenia	: L. Hurley, s	
	Nurse	: S. Warfield, c	
	Shchelkalov	: A. Budney, b	
	Mityukh	: A. Budney, b	

157. "Night on Bald Mountain" Tone Picture *(Orch.N.Rimsky-Korsakov)*

New York 11 Nov. 1957	NYPO	LP Columbia ML 5335
		LP Columbia MS 6044
		LP Odyssey 32 16 0228
		CD CBS MPK 45685

OFFENBACH, Jacques (1819-1880)

158. "Orpheus in the Underworld" Overture

Minneapolis 6 Apr. 1942	MSO	Columbia UNPUBLISHED
		RECORDING INCOMPLE

POULENC, Francis (1899-1963)

159. Concerto for Two Pianos & Orchestra in d minor

New York 15 Dec.1947	RCA	78 RCA 12-0363/65
	Arthur Whittemore & Jack Lowe	LP RCA LM 1048
	(pianos)	LP RCA WDM 1235

PROKOFIEV, Sergei Sergeievich (1891-1953)

160. Concerto for Piano & Orchestra no 3 in C major Op. 26 *

New York 16 Dec. 1945 (Live)	NBC Dimitri Mitropoulos (piano)	CD AS Disc AS 512

161. Concerto for Piano & Orchestra no 3 in C major Op. 26 *

Philadelphia 26 Jul. 1946	RHD Dimitri Mitropoulos (piano)	78 Columbia 12509/11 D LP Columbia ML 4389

162. Concerto for Piano & Orchestra no 3 in C major Op. 26 *

New York 9 Aug. 1949 (Live)	NYPSO Dimitri Mitropoulos (piano)	LP NYP 85 3/4

163. Concerto for Violin & Orchestra no 1 in D major Op. 19

New York 26 Feb. 1956 (Live)	NYPSO Isaak Stern (violin)	CD AS Disc AS 501

164. Concerto for Violin & Orchestra no 1 in D major Op. 19

New York 27 Feb. 1956	NYPSO Isaak Stern (violin)	LP Columbia ML 5243 LP CBS MP 39771 LP Philips CFL 1036 CD Sony Classical 45956

165. Concerto for Violin & Orchestra no 2 in g minor Op. 63

New York 27 Oct. 1952	NYPSO Zino Francescatti (violin)	LP Columbia ML 4648

166. "Lieutenant Kije" Suite Op. 60

New York 9 Jan. 1956	NYPSO	LP Columbia ML 5101 LP CSP P 14202

167. Overture on Hebrew Themes Op. 34

New York 1950	NYPSW Dave Weber, clarinet Jacques Margolies, 1st violin Samuel Weiss, 2nd violin David Katz, viola Avron Twerdowsky, cello William Masselos, piano	LP Decca USA DL 8511 LP Brunswick AXTL 1054 LP CHROM DCM 3215 LP CID CID 273045

SCHÖNBERG:
Concerto for Violin and Orchestra
opus 36
LOUIS KRASNER, VIOLIN, with the
PHILHARMONIC-SYMPHONY ORCHESTRA
OF NEW YORK
DIMITRI MITROPOULOS, conductor

BERG:
Concerto for Violin and Orchestra
LOUIS KRASNER, VIOLIN, with
THE CLEVELAND ORCHESTRA
ARTUR RODZINSKI, conductor

ML 4857

COLUMBIA MASTERWORKS

BORODIN: SYMPHONY NO. 2 IN B MINOR
TCHAIKOVSKY: SUITE NO. 1 IN D MAJOR

PHILHARMONIC-SYMPHONY ORCHESTRA OF NEW YORK,
DIMITRI MITROPOULOS, CONDUCTOR

ML 4902

COLUMBIA MASTERWORKS

WALLINGFORD RIEGGER
SYMPHONY NO. 3, OP. 42
EASTMAN-ROCHESTER SYMPHONY ORCHESTRA
HOWARD HANSON, Conductor

PETER MENNIN
SYMPHONY NO. 3
PHILHARMONIC-SYMPHONY
ORCHESTRA OF NEW YORK
DIMITRI MITROPOULOS, Conductor

Recorded under the auspices of the Walter W. Naumburg Foundation

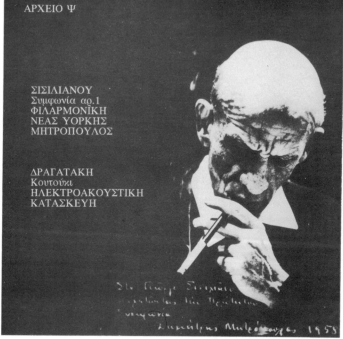

ΑΡΧΕΙΟ Ψ

ΣΙΣΙΛΙΑΝΟΥ
Συμφωνία αρ. 1
ΦΙΛΑΡΜΟΝΙΚΗ
ΝΕΑΣ ΥΟΡΚΗΣ
ΜΗΤΡΟΠΟΥΛΟΣ

ΔΡΑΓΑΤΑΚΗ
Κουτούκι
ΗΛΕΚΤΡΟΑΚΟΥΣΤΙΚΗ
ΚΑΤΑΣΚΕΥΗ

168. Quintet for Oboe, Clarinet, Violin, Viola & Bass Op. 39

New York	1950	NYPSW	LP Decca USA DL 8511
			LP Brunswick AXTI 1054
		Martin Leskow, oboe	LP CHROM DCM 3215
		Abe Goldstein, clarinet	LP CID CID 273045
		Jacques Margolies, violin	
		David Katz, viola	
		Fred Zimmerman, bass	

169. "Romeo & Juliet" Ballet Op. 64 *(Excerpts from Suites 1 & 2)*

(The Montagues & Capulets, Suite 2 no 1
Juliet the Little Girl, Suite 2 no 2
Folk Dance, Suite 1 no 1
Masks: Romeo & Mercutio Masked, Suite 1 no 5
Romeo & Juliet: Balcony Scene, Suite 1 no 6
Death of Tybalt, Suite 1 no 7
Romeo & Juliet before Parting, Suite 2 no 5
Friar Laurence, Suite 2 no 3
Romeo at Juliet's Tomb, Suite 2 no 7)

New York 11 Nov. 1957	NYPO	LP Columbia ML 5267
		LP Columbia MS 6023
		LP Odyssey 32 16 0037 M
		LP Odyssey 32 16 0038 S
		LP Philips ABL 3236
		LP CBS MP 38772
		LP CBS 60279
		CD CBS MPK 45557

170. "Scythian Suite", *(Ala & Lolly)* Op. 20

New York 27 Feb. 1955 (Live)	NYPSO	CD AS Disc AS 525

171. Symphony no 1 in D major Op. 25 "Classical"

Minneapolis 10 Jan. 1940	MSO	78 Columbia 11238/39 D
		LP Columbia RL 3021

172. Symphony no 5 in B flat major Op. 100

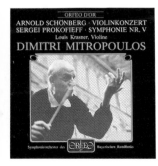

Munich 9 Jul. 1954 (Live)	BRO	LP Rococo 2082
		CD Orfeo C 204891 A

173. Symphony no 5 in B flat major Op. 100

Seattle 8 May 1955 (Live)	NYPSO	CD AS Disc AS 525

PUCCINI, Giacomo (1858-1924)

174. "La Fanciulla del West" Opera in 3 Acts *(Complete)*

(Libretto by Guelfo Civinini & Carlo Zangarini after D. Belasco's drama.)

Florence 15 Jun. 1954 (Live)	TCF & Chorus		LP Cetra LO 64
	Chorus Master	: A. Morosini	LP Cetra DOC 41
	Minnie	: E. Steber, s	*Excerpts*
	Rance	: G. G. Guelfi,b	LP GDS 4001
	Dick Johnson	: M. del Monaco,t	LP Melodram MEL 675
	Nick	: P. de Palma, t	
	Ashby	: V. Susca, bs	
	Sonora	: E. Viaro, b	
	Trin	: B. Ristori, t	
	Sid	: L. Pettini, b	
	Bello	: V. Carbonari, b	
	Harry	: V. Natali, t	
	Joe	: E. Guagni, t	
	Happy	: A. Ferrin, bs	
	Larkens	: G. Giorgetti, b	
	Billy Jackrabbit	: P. Washington, bs	
	Wowkle	: L. Didier-Gambardella, ms	
	Jake Wallace	: G. Tozzi, bs	
	Jose Castro	: M. Frosini, t	
	Postiglione	: A. Lotti-Camici, t	

175. "Madama Butterfly" Opera in 2 Acts *(Complete)*

(Libretto by Giuseppe Giacosa & Luigi Illica)

New York 15 Dec. 1956 (Live)	MOO & Chorus		LP Mov. Musica 03.027
	Chorus Master	: K. Adler	
	Butterfly	: L. Albanese, s	
	Suzuki	: R. Elias, ms	
	Kate	: M. Chambers, s	
	Pinkerton	: D. Barioni, t	
	Sharpless	: J. Brownlee, b	
	Goro	: A. de Paolis, t	
	Yamadori	: G. Cehanovsky, b	
	Bonzo	: O. Hawkins, b	
	Commissario	: L. Davidson, b	

176. "Madama Butterfly" Opera in 2 Acts *(Abridged)*

(Libretto by Giuseppe Giacosa & Luigi Illica)
Recorded for the "Book of the Month Club Inc".

New York Jan. 1957	MOO & Chorus		LP MORC MO 722
	Chorus Master	: K. Adler	
	Butterfly	: D. Kirsten, s	
	Pinkerton	: D. Barioni, t	
	Sharpless	: C. Harvuot, b	
	Suzuki	: M. Miller, c	
	Kate	: M. Chambers, s	
	Goro	: A. de Paolis, t	
	Bonzo	: O. Hawkins, b	
	Commissario	: C. Marsh, bs	
	Registrar	: L. De Cesare, b	

177. "Madama Butterfly" Opera in 2 Acts *(Complete)*

    (Libretto by Giuseppe Giacosa & Luigi Illica)

New York 16 Apr. 1960 (Live)	MOO & Chorus Chorus Master	: K. Adler	LP RDP RDIS 132-6/7/8
	Butterfly	: D. Kirsten, s	
	Suzuki	: M. Roggero, ms	
	Kate	: J. Wall, s	
	Pinkerton	: E. Fernandi, t	
	Sharpless	: M. Sereni, b	
	Goro	: C. Kullman, t	
	Yamadori	: G. Cehanovsky, b	
	Bonzo	: O. Hawkins, b	
	Commissario	: R. Reitan, bs	
	Registrar	: ? Kessler, b	

178. Intermezzo from Act 3 of the Opera "Manon Lescaut"

Philadelphia 26 Jul. 1946	RHD	78 Columbia 12981 D LP Columbia ML 2053 EP Columbia AL 1637

179. "Manon Lescaut" Opera in 4 Acts *(Complete)*

    (Libretto by Giacomo Puccini, Domenico Oliva, Marco Praga, Giulio Ricordi, Luigi Illica & Ruggero Leoncavallo.)

New York 31 Mar. 1956 (Live)	MOO & Chorus		LP Morgan Records MOR 5601 LP Cetra DOC 9
	Manon Lescaut	: L. Albanese, s	CD Melodram 27502
	Lescaut	: F. Guarrera, b	
	Des Grieux	: J. Björling, t	
	Geronte	: F. Corena, bs	
	Edmondo	: T. Hayward, t	
	Oste	: G. Cehanovsky, b	
	Un Musico	: R. Elias, ms	
	Maestro di Ballo	: A. de Paolis, t	
	Lampionaio	: J. McCracken, t	
	Sargente	: C. Marsh, bs	
	Comandante	: O. Hawkins, b	

180. "Tosca" Opera in 3 Acts *(Complete)*

    (Libretto by Giuseppe Giacosa & Luigi Illica after Victorien Sardou's drama.)

New York 8 Dec. 1955 (Live)	MOO & Chorus Chorus Master	: K. Adler	LP MET 10 LP Paragon 78-045 GDSV 52003
	Tosca	: R. Tebaldi, s	
	Cavaradossi	: R. Tucker, t	
	Scarpia	: L. Warren, b	
	Angelotti	: C. Harvuot, b	
	Sacristan	: S. Baccaloni, bs	
	Spoletta	: A. de Paolis, t	
	Sciarrone	: G. Cehanovsky, b	
	Jailer	: C. Marsh, bs	
	Shepherd	: P. Mark, t	

181. "Tosca" Opera in 3 Acts *(Complete)* *

(Libretto by Giuseppe Giacosa & Luigi Illica after Victorien Sardou's drama.)

New York 7 Jan. 1956 (Live)	MOO & Chorus		LP Cetra DOC 7
			LP RDP RDIS 132-9/10
	Chorus Master	: K. Adler	LP Ed Rosen Records ERR
			CD Cetra CDE 1003
	Tosca	: R. Tebaldi, s	
	Cavaradossi	: R. Tucker, t	*Excerpts*
	Scarpia	: L. Warren, b	LP Val. Records GML 17
	Angelotti	: C. Harvuot, b	
	Sacristan	: F. Corena, bs	
	Spoletta	: A. de Paolis, t	
	Sciarrone	: G. Cehanovsky, b	
	Jailer	: C. Marsh, bs	
	Shepherd	: P. Mark, t	

182. "Salvatelo... Io! Voi..." Scene Tosca-Scarpia from Act 2 of the Opera "Tosca"

(Ed Sullivan TV Show)

New York 25 Nov. 1956 (Live)	MOO		LP Melodram MEL 097
			LP Voce Records VOCE 13
	Tosca	: M. Callas, s	LP GOP 008/9
	Scarpia	: G. London, bs-b	CD Melodram 26011
			CD HUNT 537

183. "Tosca" Opera in 3 Acts *(Complete)*

(Libretto by Giuseppe Giacosa & Luigi Illica after Victorien Sardou's drama.)
Recorded for the "Book of the Month Club Inc".

New York Mar. 1957	MOO & Chorus		LP MORC MO 724
	Asst. Conductor	: M. Rich	
	Chorus Master	: K. Adler	
	Tosca	: D. Kirsten, s	
	Cavaradossi	: D. Barioni, t	
	Scarpia	: F. Guarrera, b	
	Angelotti	: C. Harvuot, b	
	Sacristan	: S. Baccaloni, bs	
	Spoletta	: A. de Paolis, t	
	Sciarrone	: G. Cehanovsky, b	
	Jailer	: L. Sgarro, t	

D. Mitropoulos conducts at the Hollywood Bowl. Photo Sanford Roth, Hollywood
(coll. Nick Nickson)

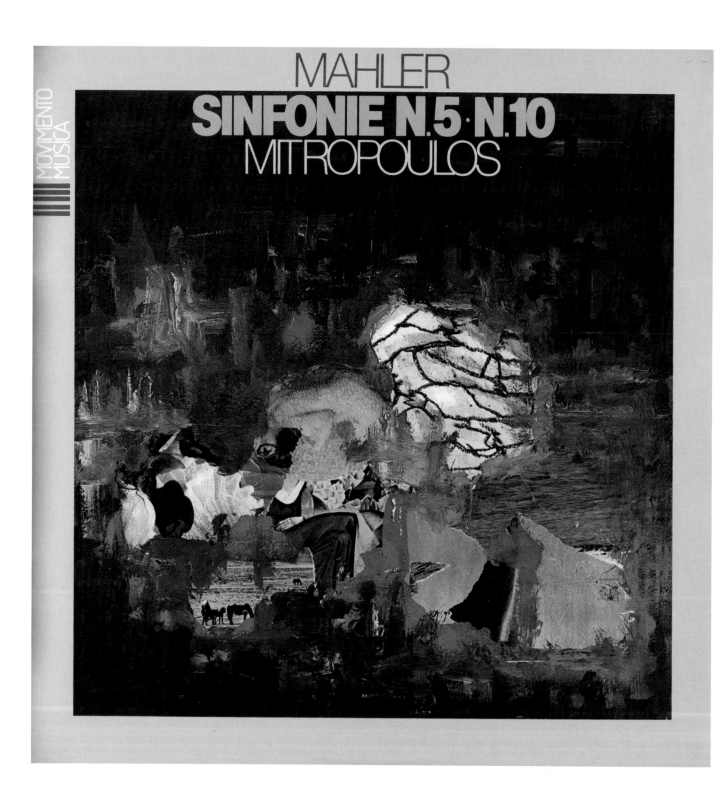

184. "Tosca" Opera in 3 Acts *(Complete)*

(Libretto by Giuseppe Giacosa & Luigi Illica after Victorien Sardou's drama.)

New York 21 Nov. 1959 (Live)	MOO & Chorus	LP UORC 148
	Chorus Master : K. Adler	

Tosca	: M. Curtis-Verna, s
Cavaradossi	: J. Björling, t
Scarpia	: C. MacNeil, b
Angelotti	: N. Scott, bs
Sacristan	: L. Davidson, b
Spoletta	: P. Franke, t
Sciarrone	: O. Hawkins, b
Jailer	: R. Reitan, bs
Shepherd	: P. Burke, t

RABAUD, Henri Benjamin (1873-1949)

185. "La Procession Nocturne" Op. 6 Symphonic Poem

New York 23 Jan. 1950	NYPSO	LP Columbia ML 2170
		LP Philips A 01604 R

RACHMANINOV, Sergei Vassilievich (1873-1943)

186. "The Isle of the Dead" Op. 29 Symphonic Poem

Minneapolis 2 Mar. 1945	MSO	78 Columbia 12271/73 D
		LP Columbia ML 4196
		LP CSP P 14151

187. Symphony no 2 in e minor Op. 27

Minneapolis 19 Jan. 1947 (1st movement) 20 Jan. 1947 (2nd, 3rd & 4th movements)	MSO	78 RCA 11-9824/29 LP RCA LM 1068

188. Symphony no 2 in e minor Op. 27

New York 2 May 1954 (Live)	NYPSO	CD AS Disc AS 524

189. "Vocalise" Op. 34, no 14 *(Orch. S. Rachmaninov)*

Seattle 8 May 1955 (Live)	NYPSO	CD AS Disc AS 524

RAVEL, Maurice (1875-1937)

190. "Pièce en Forme de Habanera" *(Arr. for Cello & Orch. by Yves Chardon)* *
    (Originally "Vocalise en forme de Habanera" for Mezzosoprano & Piano)

Minneapolis 2 Mar. 1945	MSO Yves Chardon (cello)	78 Columbia 13104 D CD NN Records NN 1002

191. "Le Tombeau de Couperin" *(Orch. M. Ravel)*

Minneapolis 6 & 7 Dec. 1941	MSO	78 Columbia 19006/07 D LP Columbia ML 2032

RIMSKY-KORSAKOV, Nikolai Andreievich (1844-1908)

192. "Bridal Procession" from "The Golden Cockerel" Suite
    (First half of the last movement)

Minneapolis 3 Dec. 1940	MSO	78 Columbia 11672 D 78 Columbia 12899 D CD NN Records NN 1003

193. "The Golden Cockerel" Suite from the Opera
    a. King Dodon in his Palace.
    c. King Dodon & the Queen of Shemakha.
    d. Bridal Procession & Lamentable Death of King Dodon.
    (Second Movement : "King Dodon on the Battlefield"
    omitted in this recording)

Minneapolis 2 Mar. 1945	MSO	78 Columbia 12150/51 D LP Columbia RL 3021

RUBINSTEIN, Anton Gregorievich (1829-1894)

194. Concerto for Piano & Orchestra no 4 in d minor Op. 70

New York 31 Mar. 1952	NYPSO Oscar Levant (piano)	LP Columbia ML 4599 LP Odyssey 32 16 0169 M

SAINT-SAËNS, Charles Camille (1835-1921)

195. Concerto for Cello & Orchestra no 1 in a minor Op. 33

New York 21 Apr. 1951	NYPSO Leonard Rose (cello)	LP Columbia ML 4425 LP CSP P 14167

196. Concerto for Piano & Orchestra no 2 in g minor Op. 22

New York 19 Apr. 1953 (Live)	NYPSO Artur Rubinstein (piano)	CD AS Disc AS 508

197. Concerto for Violin & Orchestra no 3 in b minor Op. 61

New York 23 Jan. 1950	NYPSO Zino Francescatti (violin)	78 Columbia 13106/08 D LP Columbia ML 4315 LP Columbia MS 6268 LP CBS 73143 LP Philips SBL 5219

198. "Danse Macabre" Op. 40 Symphonic Poem

New York 27 Nov. 1950	NYPSO John Corigliano (violin)	78 Columbia 13150 D LP Columbia ML 2170 LP Columbia AAL 8 LP Columbia ML 5154 LP CSP P 14205 LP Philips A 01604 R

199. "La Jeunesse d' Hercule" Op. 50 Symphonic Poem

New York 6 Jan. 1956	NYPSO	LP Columbia ML 5154 LP CSP P 14205

200. "Phaeton" Op. 39 Symphonic Poem

New York 9 Jan. 1956	NYPSO	LP Columbia ML 5154 LP CSP P 14205

201. "Le Rouet d'Omphale" Op. 31 Symphonic Poem

New York 23 Jan. 1950	NYPSO	78 Columbia 13151 D LP Columbia ML 2170 LP Columbia AAL 8 LP Columbia ML 5154 LP Philips A 01604 R

SCHMIDT, Franz (1874-1939)

202. "The Book with Seven Seals" Oratorio

Salzburg 23 Aug. 1959 (Live)	VPO Chorus of the Friends of Music Alois Forer (organ) Hilde Güden, s Ira Malaniuk, c Anton Dermota, t Fritz Wunderlich, t Walter Berry, bs	LP Melodram MEL 705

SCHÖNBERG, Arnold (1874-1951)

203. Concerto for Piano & Orchestra Op. 42

New York 3 Apr. 1958 (Live)	NYPO Glenn Gould (piano)	CD Nuova Era 013.6306

204. Concerto for Violin & Orchestra Op. 36 *

New York 1 Dec. 1952	NYPSO Louis Krassner (violin)	LP Columbia ML 4857

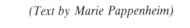

205. Concerto for Violin & Orchestra Op. 36

Munich 9 Jul. 1954 (Live)	BRO Louis Krassner (violin)	CD Orfeo C 204891 A

206. Concerto for Violin & Orchestra Op. 36

Cologne 16 Jul. 1954 (Live)	CRO Louis Krassner (violin)	LP GUN-MAR GM 2006

207. "Erwartung" Monodram Op. 17
(Text by Marie Pappenheim)

New York 18 Nov. 1951 (Live)	NYPSO Dorothy Dow, s	LP AS Disc AS 540

208. "Erwartung" Monodram Op. 17
(Text by Marie Pappenheim. Premiere Recording)

New York 19 Nov. 1951	NYPSO Dorothy Dow, s	LP Columbia ML 4524 LP Philips ABL 3393

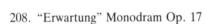

209. "Serenade" for Septet & Baritone Op. 24 *
(Premiere Recording)

New York Dec. 1949	ISCM	LP Count-Esot 501 M LP Count-Esot 5501 S LP Count-Esot MC 20005 LP Concerthall CM 2175
	Clark Brody, clarinet Eric Simon, bass clarinet Sal Piccardi, mandolin John Smith, guitar Louis Krassner, violin Ralph Mersh, viola Seymour Barab, cello Warren Galjour, b	

210. "Transfigured Night" Op. 4 for String Orchestra

New York 3 Mar. 1958	NYPO Strings	LP Columbia ML 5285 LP Columbia MS 6007 LP Odyssey 32 16 0298 S

D. Mitropoulos during the making of one of his first grammophone records. Photo from the album "Ovation" The Minnesota Orchestra's 75th Anniversary.

211. Variations for Orchestra Op. 31

Salzburg 21 Aug. 1960   BPO   CD Nuova Era 013.6306
(Live)

SCHULLER, Gunther (1925-   )

212. Symphony for Brass and Percussion Op. 16 *
    (Premiere Recording)

New York 14 Jun. 1956   BEJ & CMS   LP Columbia CL-941

Trumpets	: John Ware (solo)
(1st Section)	: Ted Weiss
	: Joseph Alessi
(2nd Section)	: Mel Broiles
	: Carmine Fornarotto
	: Isidore Blank
Horns	: Joseph Singer (solo)
	: Roy Alonge
	: Arthur Sussman
	: GUNTHER SCHULLER
Trombones	: Gordon Pulis (solo)
	: Gil Cohen
	: John Clark
Baritones	: John Swallow (solo)
	: Ronald Ricketts
Tuba	: Bill Barber
Timpani & Percussion	: Dick Horowitz

SCHUMANN, Robert (1810-1856)

213. Concerto for Piano & Orchestra in a minor Op. 54
    (A. Benedetti-Michelangeli's debut performance in America)

New York 21 Nov. 1948   NYPSO   LP Rococco 2024
(Live)   A.Benedetti-Michelangeli (piano)   LP Arioso Historical 15.006
                                                      CD AS Disc AS 321

214. Concerto for Piano & Orchestra in a minor Op. 54

New York 10 Feb. 1952   NYPSO   CD Melodram 18.024
(Live)   Dame Myra Hess (piano)

215. Symphony no 1 in B flat major Op. 38 "Spring"

New York 11 Nov. 1956   NYPO   CD AS Disc AS 501
(Live)

216. Symphony no 2 in C major Op. 61

| Minneapolis 3 Dec. 1940 | MSO | 78 Columbia 11761/65 D |
| | | LP Columbia RL 3025 |

217. Symphony no 3 in E flat major Op. 97 "Rhenish"

Minneapolis 20 Jan. 1947	MSO	78 RCA 12-0020/23
		LP RCA LM 1067
		LP RCA LBC 1058

SCRIABIN, Alexander Nicolaievich (1872-1915)

218. "Poem of Ecstasy" Op. 54

| New York 20 Mar. 1953 | NYPSO | LP Columbia ML 4731 |
| | William Vacchiano (trumpet) | LP CSP P 14184 |

219. "Poem of Ecstasy" Op. 54

| New York 19 Apr. 1953 | NYPSO | CD AS Disc AS 508 |
| (Live) | William Vacchiano (trumpet) | |

220. "Poem of Fire, Prometheus" Op. 60

| New York 20 Mar. 1953 | NYPSO | LP Columbia ML 4731 |
| | Leonid Hambro (piano) | LP CSP P 14184 |

SESSIONS, Roger (1896-1988)

221. Symphony no 2
(Walter W. Naumburg Foundation American Composition Award. Premiere Recording)

New York 16 Jan. 1950	NYPSO	78 Columbia 13095/98 D
		LP Columbia ML 2120
		LP Columbia ML 4784
		LP CRI SD 278
		CD CRI 573

SHERWOOD, Gordon (1929-   )

222. Introduction & Allegro *
(Winning composition of the Annual Gershwin Memorial Award World Premiere Performance)

| New York 5 May 1957 | NYPO | CD AS Disc AS 543 |
| (Live) | | |

SHOSTAKOVICH, Dmitri Dmitrievich (1906-1975)

223. Concerto for Violin & Orchestra no 1 in a minor Op. 99
 (D. Oistrakh's debut performance in America. American Premiere Performance)

New York 1 Jan. 1956   NYPSO   LP Cetra DOC 6
(Live)   David Oistrakh (violin)

224. Concerto for Violin & Orchestra no 1 in a minor Op. 99

New York 2 Jan. 1956   NYPSO   LP Columbia ML 5077
                              David Oistrakh (violin)   LP CBS MP 39771
                                                         LP Philips ABL 3101
                                                         CD CBS 39771

225. Symphony no 5 in d minor Op. 47

New York 1 Dec. 1952   NYPSO   LP Columbia ML 4739
                                                         LP CSP P 14185

226. Symphony no 10 in e minor Op. 93 *

New York 18 Oct. 1954   NYPSO   LP Columbia ML 4959
                                                         LP Odyssey 32 16 0123
                                                         LP CBS 61457
                                                         LP Philips ABL 3052
                                                         LP Philips A 01.175
                                                         CD CBS MPK 45698

SICILIANOS, Yorgos (1920-   )

227. Symphony no 1 Op. 14 *
 (World Premiere Performance)

New York 1 Mar. 1958   NYPO   LP ARCHIO PSI 91065
(Live)

SIEGMEISTER, Elie (1909-   )

228. "Ozark Set"
 (Premiere Recording)

Minneapolis 2 Mar. 1945   MSO   78 Columbia 12295/96 D
                                                         LP Columbia ML 2123
                                                         LP OMR ORS 73116

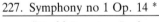

SKALKOTTAS, Nikos (1904-1949)

229. "Four Greek Dances"
*(Peloponissiakos, Ipirotikos
Hostianos, Kleftikos)*

New York 9 Jan. 1956	NYPSO	LP Columbia ML 5335 EP Philips 409152 AE EP CBS CBSI BA 307001

STRAUSS, Richard (1864-1949)

230. "Also Sprach Zarathustra" Op. 30 Symphonic Poem
(Concert to commemorate the 10th anniversary of R. Strauss' death)

Cologne 7 Sep. 1959 (Live)	CRO	LP Cetra DOC 13 CD HUNT 508 CD Virtuoso 2697032

231. "Burleske" in d minor for Piano & Orchestra

New York 9 Feb. 1958 (Live)	NYPO Rudolf Serkin (piano)	CD HUNT HN 581

232. "Tod und Verklärung" Op. 24 Symphonic Poem *
(Concert dedicated to the memory of Guido Cantelli)

New York 2 Dec. 1956 (Live)	NYPO	LP NYP 881/2 CD HUNT HN 583

233. "Die Frau ohne Schatten" Op. 65 Symphonic Fantasy from the Opera

New York 11 Feb. 1954 (Live)	NYPSO	CD HUNT HN 581

234. "Don Juan" Op. 20 Symphonic Poem

New York 26 Oct. 1956 (Live)	NYPO	CD HUNT HN 581

235. "Don Quixote" Op. 35 Variations on a Knightly Theme
(Concert to commemorate the 10th anniversary of R. Strauss' death)

Cologne 7 Sep. 1959 (Live)	CRO Paul Schröer (viola) Alwin Bauer (cello)	LP Cetra DOC 13 CD HUNT 508

236. "Eine Alpensinfonie" Op. 64

Venice 19 Sep. 1956 (Live)	VPO	CD HUNT HN 581

237. "Electra" Op. 58 Opera in 1 Act *(Complete)*.
(Libretto by Hugo von Hofmannsthal)

New York 25 Dec. 1949 (Live)	NYPSO		LP RHR 5101/02
	Electra	: A. Varnay, s	LP OTARC OTA 4
	Klytemnestra	: E. Nikolaidi, c	
	Chrysothemis	: I. Jessner, s	
	Orestes	: H. Janssen, b	
	Aegisthus	: F. Jagel, t	
	Tutor	: M. Rhodes, bs	
	First Maid	: M. Stockton, s	
	Second Maid	: E. Evans, s	
	Third Maid	: E. Warren, s	
	Fourth Maid	: B. Dame, s	

238. "Electra" Op. 58 Opera in 1 Act *(Complete)*
(Libretto by Hugo von Hofmannsthal.
Recorded during actual performances.)

Florence 16 & 18 May 1950	MMF & Chorus		LP Cetra Soria CS 1209
	Electra	: A. Konetzni, s	LP Cetra Soria CS 519/20
	Klytemnestra	: M. Mödl, c	LP Cetra LPO 2010
	Chrysothemis	: D. Ilitsch, s	LP Cetra TRV 07
	Orestes	: H. Braun, b	LP Everest S-459/2
	Aegisthus	: F. Klarwein, t	LP Turnabout/Vox THS 65040
	Tutor	: W. Felden, bs	
	Confidante	: D. Frass, s	
	Train-Bearer	: A. Michalsky, s	
	Young Servant	: J. Schmidinger, t	
	Old Servant	: L. Pantscheff, bs	
	Overseer	: C. Markus, s	
	First Maid	: G. Schuster, s	
	Second Maid	: P. Batic, s	
	Third Maid	: K. Sabo, s	
	Fourth Maid	: D. Schmedes, s	
	Fifth Maid	: F. Riegler, s	

239. "Electra" Op. 58 Opera in 1 Act *(Complete)*
(Libretto by Hugo von Hofmannsthal.)

Salzburg 7 Aug. 1957 (Live)	VPO		LP Cetra LO 83
	Vienna State Opera Chorus		LP Discocorp SID 731
	Electra	: I. Borkh, s	CD Nuova Era 2241/42
	Klytemnestra	: J. Madeira, c	
	Chrysothemis	: L. della Casa, s	
	Orestes	: K. Böhme, bs	
	Aegisthus	: M. Lorenz, t	
	Tutor	: A. Pernerstorfer, bs-b	
	Confidante	: A. Felbermayer, s	
	Train-Bearer	: K. Loraine, s	
	Young Servant	: E. Majkut, t	
	Old Servant	: G. Littasy, bs	
	Overseer	: A. Gerber-Candy, s	
	First Maid	: K. Meyer, c	
	Second Maid	: S. Draxler, c	
	Third Maid	: S. Wagner, ms	
	Fourth Maid	: M. Horne, c	
	Fifth Maid	: L. Otto, s	

CARNEGIE HALL

Photo EDITTA SHERMAN

Dimitri Mitropoulos

285-4-22A-51   ALFRED SCOTT -:- PUBLISHER -:- 156 FIFTH AVENUE, NEW YORK

Front page of the New York Philharmonic - Symphony Orchestra's programme of the concert given at the Carnegie Hall on April 22, 1951.

(coll. S.A. Arfanis)

240. "Allein! Weh,ganz allein" Electra's Monologue from the Opera "Electra" Op. 58

(Concert to commemorate the 10th anniversary of R. Strauss' death)

Cologne 7 Sep. 1959	CRO		LP Cetra DOC 13
(Live)			CD HUNT HN 581
	Electra	: A. Varnay, s	

241. "Salome" Op. 54 Opera in 1 Act *(Complete)*

(The Libretto is Oscar Wilde's play translated in German by Hedwig Lachmann.)

New York 8 Jan. 1955	MOO		LP HOPE 238
(Live)			
	Salome	: C. Goltz, s	
	Herodias	: B. Thebom, c	
	Herod	: R. Vinay, t	
	Jokanaan	: P. Schöffler, bs-b	
	Naraboth	: B. Sullivan, t	
	Page	: M. Miller, c	
	First Nazarene	: N. Moscona, bs	
	Second Nazarene	: C. Marsh, bs	
	First Jew	: G. Carelli, t	
	Second Jew	: J. McCracken, t	
	Third Jew	: A. De Paolis, t	
	Fourth Jew	: P. Franke, t	
	Fifth Jew	: G. Pechner, b	
	First Soldier	: N. Scott, bs	
	Second Soldier	: L. Alvary, b	
	Cappadocian	: O. Hawkins, b	
	Slave	: V. Georgiou, s	

242. "Dance of the Seven Veils" from the Opera "Salome" Op. 54

| New York 3 Nov. 1956 | NYPO | LP Columbia ML 5198 |

243. "Salome" Op. 54 Opera in 1 Act *(Complete)*

(The Libretto is Oscar Wilde's play translated in German by Hedwig Lachmann.)

New York 8 Feb. 1958	MOO		LP Cetra LO 82
(Live)			
	Salome	: I. Borkh, s	
	Herodias	: B. Thebom, c	
	Herod	: R. Vinay, t	
	Jokanaan	: M. Harrell, b	
	Naraboth	: G. Gari, t	
	Page	: M. Roggero, ms	
	First Nazarene	: W. Wilderman, b	
	Second Nazarene	: C. Marsh, bs	
	First Jew	: A. De Paolis, t	
	Second Jew	: G. Carelli, t	
	Third Jew	: R. Nagy, t	
	Fourth Jew	: P. Franke, t	
	Fifth Jew	: L. Davidson, b	
	First Soldier	: L. Sgarro, t	
	Second Soldier	: N. Scott, bs	
	Cappadocian	: O. Hawkins, b	
	Slave	: M. Allen, s	

244. "Sinfonia Domestica" Op. 53

New York Apr. 1950 (Live)	NYPSO	CD HUNT HN 583

245. "Sinfonia Domestica" Op. 53

Cologne 19 Jul. 1957 (Live)	CRO	CD HUNT HN 581

STRAVINSKY, Igor Feodorovich (1882-1971)

246. "Petrouchka" Ballet *(1911 version)*

New York 5 Mar. 1951	NYPSO	LP Columbia	ML 4438
		LP Philips	GBR 6519
		LP Philips	A 01.104
		LP Philips	S 06.641
		LP CSP	P 14169

SWANSON, Howard (1907-1978)

247. "Night Music"

New York 1950	NYPSW	LP Decca USA	DL 8511
		LP Brunswick	AXTL 1054
		LP CHROM	DCM 3215
	Jacques Margolies, 1st violin	LP CID	CID 273045
	Samuel Weiss, 2nd violin		
	David Katz, viola		
	Avron Twerdowsky, cello		
	Fred Zimmerman, bass		
	Sebastian Caratelli, flute		
	Albert Goltzer, oboe		
	Dave Weber, clarinet		
	Harold Goltzer, bassoon		
	David Rattner, horn		

TRAVIS, Roy Elihu (1922-)

248. "Symphonic Allegro"
(Winning Composition of the 7th Annual Gershwin Memorial Award, sponsored by Victory Lodge B'nai B'rith)

New York 4 Jan. 1952	NYPSO	LP Columbia AAL 16

ΟΚΤΩ ΛΑ·Ι·ΚΑΙ ΣΥΝΑΥΛΙΑΙ
ΤΗΣ ΣΥΜΦΩΝΙΚΗΣ ΟΡΧΗΣΤΡΑΣ
ΔΟΘΕΙΣΑΙ ΕΝ ΤΩ ΘΕΑΤΡΩ «ΟΛΥΜΠΙΑ»

ΠΡΩΤΗ ΛΑ·Ι·ΚΗ ΣΥΝΑΥΛΙΑ

Κυριακὴ 17 Νοεμβρίου 1929, ὥραν 11 π. μ.

Διευθυντὴς Ὀρχήστρας
Δ. ΜΗΤΡΟΠΟΥΛΟΣ

Π ρ ό γ ρ α μ μ α.

R. Wagner   *Faust*, εἰσαγωγή.
                Ὑπὸ τῆς ὀρχήστρας (πρώτη ἐκτέλεσις).
S. Prokofieff   *Κοντσέρτο διὰ κλειδοκύμβαλον ἀρ. 3.*
                I Andante — Allegro. II Andante. Tema con varia-
                zioni. III Allegro scherzando.
                Ὁ *κ. Δ. Μητρόπουλος* καὶ ἡ ὀρχήστρα (πρώτη ἐκτέλεσις).
L. van Beethoven *Συμφωνία, ἀρ. 3 (᾿Ηρωϊκὴ) εἰς Μι ♭*
                I Allegro con brio. II Marcia funebre Adazio assai.
                III Scherzo. Allegro vivace. IV Finale. Allegro
                molto. Ὑπὸ τῆς ὀρχήστρας.

Programme of the concert given by the Athens Odeon Orchestra at the Olympia Theatre on November 17, 1929
when S. Prokofiev's 3rd Piano concerto was performed for the first time in Athens.
D. Mitropoulos pianist - conductor.

ΠΡΩΤΗ ΣΥΝΑΥΛΙΑ ΣΥΝΔΡΟΜΗΤΩΝ

Τρίτη 18 Νοεμβρίου 1930, ὥραν 6.15 μ.μ.

Διευθυντὴς Ὀρχήστρας :   Σολίστ :
Δ ΜΗΤΡΟΠΟΥΛΟΣ   Ὁ διάσημος καλλιτέχνης τοῦ πιάνου
                                   ERNÖ DOHNANYI

Ἡ *Γενικὴ Δοκιμὴ* ἐδόθη τὴν Κυριακὴν 16 Νοεμβρίου ὥραν 11 π. μ.

Π ρ ό γ ρ α μ μ α

Bach-Μητροπούλου *Φαντασία καὶ φούγκα εἰς σολ ἐλ.*
                δι' ἐκκλ. ὄργανον, ἐνορχηστρωθεῖσα ὑπὸ τοῦ κ. *Δ. Μη-
                τροπούλου.*
                I Maestoso II Fuga (Allegro moderato)
                Ὑπὸ τῆς ὀρχήστρας (πρώτη ἐκτέλεσις).
L. van Beethoven *Κοντσέρτο ἀρ. 4.*
                I Allegro moderato II Andante con moto III Rondo-
                Vivace
                Ὁ *κ. Dohnanyi* καὶ ἡ ὀρχήστρα.
G. Mahler   *Συμφωνία ἀρ. 1.*
                I, II, III, IV.
                Ὑπὸ τῆς ὀρχήστρας.

Programme of the concert given by the Athens Odeon Orchestra at the Olympia Theatre on November 18, 1930
when D. Mitropoulos' transcription of J.S. Bach's Fantasy & Fugue was performed for the first time in Athens.

TCHAIKOVSKY, Piotr Ilyich (1840-1893)

249. "Capriccio Italien" Op. 45

New York 22 Apr. 1957	NYPO	LP Columbia ML 5335
		LP Columbia MS 6044
		LP Odyssey 32 16 0228 S
		LP CBS 73143 S
		CD CBS MPK 45699

250. Concerto for Piano & Orchestra no 1 in B flat major Op. 23

Minneapolis 16 Nov. 1947	MSO	78 RCA 11-9776/79
	Artur Rubinstein (piano)	LP RCA LM 1028
		LP HMV FALP 275
		LP RCA VLS H 5502 S
		LP RCA WDM 1159

251. Concerto for Violin & Orchestra in D major Op. 35

New York 27 Mar. 1954	NYPSO	LP Columbia ML 4965
	Zino Francescatti (violin)	LP Philips ABL 3159
		LP Philips A 01.214
		LP CBS Sony 20 AC 1900
		Excerpts
		LP Columbia D-2
		(Second Movement:
		Canzonetta-Andante)

252. "Eugene Oniegin" Op. 24 Opera in 3 Acts *(Complete)*

*(Libretto by the composer & Konstantin S. Schilowski
after A. Puschkin's poem. Sung in English. Text by Henry Reese.)*

New York 7 Dec. 1957	MOO & Chorus	LP GOP 50
(Live)	Chorus Master : K. Adler	CD GOP 707
	Oniegin : G. London, bs-b	
	Lenski : R. Tucker, t	
	Tatiana : L. Amara, s	
	Olga : R. Elias, ms	
	Gremin : G. Tozzi, bs	
	Larina : M. Lipton, c	
	Filippyevna : B. Amparan, c	
	Un Tenente : L. Sgarro, t	
	Triquet : A. De Paolis, t	
	Zaretski : G. Cehanovsky, b	

253. "Eugene Oniegin" Op. 24 Opera in 3 Acts *(Abridged)*

(Libretto by the composer & Konstantin S. Schilowski
after A. Puschkin's poem. Sung in English. Text by Henry Reese.
Recorded for the "Book of the Month Club Inc".)

New York Dec. 1957	MOO & Chorus		LP MORC MO 824
	Asst. Conductor	: I. Strasfogel	
	Chorus Master	: K. Adler	
	Oniegin	: F. Guarrera, b	
	Lenski	: R. Tucker, t	
	Tatiana	: L. Amara, s	
	Olga	: R. Elias, ms	
	Gremin	: G. Tozzi, bs	
	Larina	: M. Lipton, c	
	Filippyevna	: B. Amparan, c	
	Zaretski	: G. Cehanovsky, b	

254. "Marche Slave" Op. 31

New York 11 Nov. 1957	NYPO	LP Columbia ML 5335
		LP Columbia MS 6044
		LP Odyssey 32 16 0228 S
		CD CBS MPK 45699

255. Suite no 1 in D major Op. 43

(Third Movement "Intermezzo" omitted in this recording)

New York 18 Oct. &	NYPSO	LP Columbia ML 4966
17 Nov. 1954		LP CSP P 14195
		LP Philips ABL 3079

256. Symphony no 2 in c minor Op. 17 "Little Russian"

Minneapolis 10 &	MSO	78 Columbia 12527/31 D
11 Mar. 1946		LP Columbia ML 4252
		LP Columbia RL 6623
		LP CSP P 14158

257. Symphony no 4 in f minor Op. 36

Minneapolis 10 &	MSO	78 Columbia 11595/99 D
22 Jan. 1940		LP Columbia RL 3007
(Partial remake 26 Nov. 1940)		

258. Symphony no 5 in e minor Op. 64

New York 27 Mar. 1954	NYPSO	LP Columbia CL 764
		LP Columbia ML 5075
		LP CSP P 14199
		LP Philips GBL 5631
		LP Philips SBL 5205
		LP Philips S 04.605 L

259. Symphony no 6 in b minor Op. 74 "Pathétique"

New York 11 Nov. 1957	NYPO	LP Columbia ML 5235

LP Columbia MS 6006
LP Odyssey 32 16 0216
LP CBS Sonny 13 AC 952
LP Philips SABL 104
LP Philips A 01. 366 L
CD CBS MPK 45699
Excerpts
LP Columbia SF 1
   (Allegro Vivo section,
   of First Movement)

VAUGHAN-WILLIAMS, Ralph (1872-1958)

260. "Fantasia on a Theme by Thomas Tallis" for String Orchestra

Minneapolis 2 Mar. 1945	MSO Strings	78 Columbia 12873/74 D

LP Columbia ML 4196
LP CSP P 14151

261. "Fantasia on a Theme by Thomas Tallis" for String Orchestra

New York 3 Mar. 1958	NYPO Strings	LP Columbia ML 5285

LP Columbia MS 6007
LP CBS 73143
LP Odyssey 32 16 0298 S

262. Symphony no 4 in f minor

New York 9 Jan. 1956	NYPSO	LP Columbia ML 5158

LP CSP CML 5158
LP CBS 61432 M

VERDI, Giuseppe (1813-1901)

263. "Un Ballo in Maschera" Opera in 3 Acts *(Abridged)*

    (Libretto by Antonio Somma after E. Scribe's drama "Gustave III")

New York 9 Jan. 1955	MOO		LP RCA LM 1911
(Act 1)			LP RCA LM 20146
21 Jan. 1955	Riccardo	: J. Peerce, t	LP RCA LM 1932
(Acts 2 & 3)	Renato	: L. Warren, b	LP HMV ALP 1476
	Amelia	: Z. Milanov, s	LP Melodiya D-031891
	Ulrica	: M. Anderson, ms	CD RCA 7911-2 RG
	Oscar	: R. Peters, s	*Excerpts*

LP RCA RL 85177 (8)
Act 1: Re dell'Abisso
w.M. Anderson, ms

D. Mitropoulos conducts M. Kalomiris' opera "The Masterbuilder", January 10 12, 1930
(coll S.A. Arfanis)

66

264. "Un Ballo in Maschera" Opera in 3 Acts *(Complete)*

(Libretto by Antonio Somma after E. Scribe's drama "Gustave III")

New York 22 Jan. 1955 (Live)	MOO & Chorus		LP Cetra LO 4 LP Foyer FO 1020 CD Foyer 2 CF-2004
	Riccardo	: R. Tucker, t	*Excerpts*
	Amelia	: Z. Milanov, s	LP Val. Records GML 13
	Ulrica	: J. Madeira, c	
	Renato	: J. Metternich,b	
	Oscar	: R. Peters, s	
	Silvano	: C. Marsh, b	
	Sam	: N. Moscona, bs	
	Tom	: N. Scott, bs	
	Giudice	: J. McCracken, t	
	Servo	: C. Anthony, t	

265. "Ernani" Opera in 4 Acts *(Complete)*

(Libretto by Francesco Maria Piave after V. Hugo's drama)

New York 29 Dec. 1956 (Live)	MOO & Chorus		LP Cetra LO 12 LP Foyer FO 1021 LP MRF Records MRF 6
	Ernani	: M. del Monaco,t	CD Foyer 2CF 2006
	Don Carlo	: L. Warren, b	*Excerpts*
	Silva	: C. Siepi, bs	LP GDS 4001
	Elvira	: Z. Milanov, s	LP Melodram MEL 675
	Giovanna	: H. Vanni, s	CD Virtuoso 2697132
	Don Riccardo	: J. McCracken, t	
	Iago	: G. Cehanovsky, b	

266. "Ernani" Opera in 4 Acts *(Complete)*

(Libretto by Francesco Maria Piave after V. Hugo's drama)

Florence 14 Jun. 1957 (Live)	TCF & Chorus		LP Morgan Records MOR 5702
	Chorus Master	: A. Morosini	LP Cetra DOC 36 CD Melodram 27016
			Excerpts
	Ernani	: M. del Monaco, t	LP Foyer 1035
	Don Carlo	: E. Bastianini, b	LP Joker SM 1299
	Silva	: B. Christoff,bs	LP Val. Records GML 33
	Elvira	: A. Cerquetti, s	LP Mov. Musica 01.012
	Giovanna	: L. Boni, s	
	Don Riccardo	: A. Cesarini, t	
	Iago	: A. Neagu, b	

267. "La Forza del Destino" Opera in 4 Acts *(Complete)*

(Libretto by Francesco Maria Piave.)

Florence 14 Jun. 1953 (Live)	TCF & Chorus		LP Cetra LO 17
	Chorus Master	: A. Morosini	LP Turnabout/Vox 65117/19
			LP Foyer FO 1019
	Leonora	: R. Tebaldi, s	CD Foyer 3 CF-2005
	Preziosilla	: F. Barbieri, ms	*Excerpts*
	Curra	: A. Vercelli, s	LP Foyer 1035
	Don Alvaro	: M. del Monaco, t	LP Val. Records GML 7
	Don Carlo	: A. Protti, b	LP Mov. Musica 01.012
	Guardiano	: C. Siepi, bs	
	Melitone	: R. Capecchi, bs	
	Calatrava	: S. Maionica, bs	
	Alcade	: G. Giorgetti, b	
	Trabuco	: P. de Palma, t	
	Chirurgo	: W. Finessi, b	

268. "La Forza del Destino" Overture

Florence 17 Jun. 1953 (Live)	MMF	LP Cetra DOC 64

269. "La Forza del Destino" Opera in 4 Acts *(Complete)*

(Libretto by Fracesco Maria Piave.)

Vienna 23 Sep. 1960 (Live)	VPO		LP Melodram MEL 023
	Vienna State Opera Chorus		CD GDS 31022
	Leonora	: A. Stella, s	
	Preziosilla	: G. Simionato, ms	
	Curra	: H. Ludwig, ms	
	Don Alvaro	: G. Di Stefano, t	
	Don Carlo	: E. Bastianini, b	
	Guardiano	: W. Kreppel, bs	
	Melitone	: K. Dönch, bs	
	Calatrava	: L. Welter, bs	
	Alcade	: H. Pröglhöf, bs	
	Trabuco	: H. Meyer-Welfing, t	
	Chirurgo	: F. Bierbach, b	

270. "Simon Boccanegra" Opera in a Prologue and 3 Acts *(Complete)*

(Libretto by Francesco Maria Piave.)

New York 2 Apr. 1960 (Live)	MOO & Chorus		LP Foyer FO 1023
			LP Estro Armonico E/A 023
			LP MRF Records MRF 84
	Boccanegra	: F. Guarrera, b	
	Fiesco	: G. Tozzi, bs	
	Paolo	: E. Flagello, bs	
	Pietro	: N. Scott, bs	
	Maria-Amelia	: Z. Milanov, s	
	Adorno	: C. Bergonzi, t	
	Un Capitano	: R. Nagy, t	
	Un Ancella	: M. Janger, s	

VIOTTI, Giovanni Battista (1755-1824)

271. Concerto for Violin & Orchestra no 22 in a minor

New York 18 Oct. 1953 (Live)	NYPSO Jehudi Menuhin (violin)	LP Rococo 2024

WAGNER, Richard (1813-1883)

272. "Die Walküre" Music Drama in 3 Acts *(Complete)*
(Libretto by the composer)

New York 2 Feb. 1957   MOO   LP Melodram MEL 004
(Live)   LP Raritas OPR 403

Brünnhilde	: M. Harshaw, s	CD Nuova Era 2211/3
Sieglinde	: M. Schech, s	
Fricka	: B. Thebom, ms	
Siegmund	: R. Vinay, t	
Wotan	: O. Edelmann, bs-b	
Hunding	: K. Böhme, bs	
Helmwige	: G. Lind, s	
Gerhlide	: C. Ordassy, s	
Ortlinde	: H. Krall, s	
Rossweise	: S. Warfield, c	
Grimgerde	: M. Lipton, c	
Waltraute	: M. Moll, c	
Siegrune	: R. Elias, ms	
Schwertleite	: B. Amparan, c	

273. "Die Walküre" Music Drama in 3 Acts *(Scenes)*
(Libretto by the composer. Recorded for the "Book of the Month Club Inc".)

New York Feb. 1957	MOO	LP MORC MO 728
Brünnhilde	: M. Harshaw, s	
Sieglinde	: M. Schech, s	
Fricka	: B. Thebom, ms	
Siegmund	: R. Vinay, t	
Wotan	: H. Uhde, bs-b	
Hunding	: N. Scott, bs	
Helmwige	: G. Lind, s	
Gerhilde	: C. Ordassy, s	
Ortlinde	: H. Krall, s	
Rossweisse	: S. Warfield, c	
Grimgerde	: M. Lipton, c	
Waltraute	: M. Moll, c	
Siegrune	: R. Elias, ms	
Schwertleite	: B. Amparan, c	

274. "Wotans's Farewell & Magic Fire Music" from the Music Drama "Die Walküre"

New York 20 Feb. 1957   MOO   LP Melodram MEL 094
(Live)

                             Wotan   : H. Uhde, bs-b

275. "Götterdämmerung" Music Drama in 3 Acts *(Act 3, Complete)*
    (Libretto by the composer)

New York 30 Oct. 1955   NYPSO   CD AS Disc AS 549
(Live)

                             Brünnhilde   : A. Varnay, s
                             Siegfried   : R. Vinay, t
                             Gutrune   : L. Amara, s
                             Gunther   : C. Harvuot, b
                             Hagen   : L. Vichegonov, bs
                             Woglinde   : S. Vartenissian, s
                             Wellgunde   : H. Glaz, ms
                             Flosshilde   : R. Elias, ms

276. "Forest Murmurs" from Act 2 of the Music Drama "Siegfried"

New York 30 Oct. 1955   NYPSO   CD AS Disc AS 549
(Live)

WALTON, William Turner (1902-1983)

277. "Portsmouth Point" Overture

Minneapolis 10 Mar. 1946   MSO   78 Columbia 13755 D
                                                                         LP NH Records NH 1001

WEBER, Carl Maria Ernst von (1786-1826)

278. "Jubel" Overture Op. 59

Minneapolis 11 Mar. 1946   MSO   78 Columbia 12891 D
                                                                         LP Columbia RL 3038

WEBERN, Anton von (1883-1945)

279. Passacaglia for Orchestra, Op. 1

New York 23 Jan. 1960   NYPO   CD AS Disc AS 540
(Live)

WEINBERGER, Jaromir (1896-1967)

280. "Polka & Fugue" from the Opera "Schwanda the Bagpiper"

Minneapolis 20 Jan. 1947   MSO   78 RCA 12-0019
78 RCA 49-0287
CD NN Records NN 1002

281. "Polka & Fugue" from the Opera "Schwanda the Bagpiper"

New York 2 Nov. 1956   NYPO   LP Columbia ML 5198

WOLF-FERRARI, Ermanno (1876-1948)

282. "Intermezzo" from Act 2 of the Opera "I Gioielli della Madonna"

Philadelphia 26 Jul. 1946   RHD   78 Columbia 12981 D
LP Columbia ML 2053
EP Columbia A-1637

283. "Intermezzo" from Act 3 of the Opera "I Gioielli della Madonna"

Philadelphia 26 Jul. 1946   RHD   78 Columbia 12982 D
LP Columbia ML 2053
EP Columbia A-1637

ZIMMERMANN, Bernd Alois (1918-1970)

284. Concerto for Oboe & Orchestra

(Concert to commemorate the 100th anniversary of G. Mahler's birth)

Cologne 31 Aug. 1959   CRO   LP Cetra DOC 5
(Live)   Lothar Faber (oboe)

Advertisement for RCA Victor recording of M. Mussorgsky's Boris Godunov
(coll. Nick Nickson)

APPENDIX A / ΠΑΡΑΡΤΗΜΑ Α

SOURCES / ΠΗΓΕΣ

Foreign / Ξενόγλωσσες

Baker's Biographical Dictionary of Musicians 6th Edition Completely Revised by Nicolas Slonimsky
Schirmer Books New York 1978

Clough, Francis F. & Cuming, G. J. *The World's Encyclopaedia of Recorded Music*
Main Volume 1926-Apr. 1950. London, The London Gramophone Corporation in Association with
Sidgwick & Jackson Ltd. 1952

Supplement I Apr. 1950-May/June 1951 London, The London Gramophone Corporation in Association
with Sidgwick & Jackson Ltd. 1952

Supplement II 1951-1953 London, The London Gramophone Corporation in Association with The Decca
Company Ltd. 1953 Associate Editor E. A. Hughes.

Supplement III 1953-1955. London, The London Gramophone Corporation in Association with The
Decca Company Ltd. 1957 Associate Editor E. A. Hughes
Research Associate Angela Noble

Disques de Longue-Durée Printemps 1956 no 11 Catalogue Complet Permanent Paris,
Edition de La Revue Disques.

Disques de Longue-Durée 1958 no Double 18-19
Catalogue Generale annuel Paris, Edition de la Revue Disques.

Guide Français du Disque no 1 1946-1952
Catalogue Generale annuel Paris, Edition de la Revue Disques.

Holmes, John L. *Conductors on Record* London, Victor Gollancz Ltd. 1982

Kaut, Josef. *Die Salzburger Festspiele 1920-1981* Salzburg, Residenz Verlag 1982

Kennedy, Michael. *The Concise Oxford Dictionary of Music* Third Edition based on the original publication by
Percy Scholes. Oxford, Oxford University Press 1985

Kolodin, Irving. *The Metropolitan Opera 1883-1966* New York, Alfred A. Knopf 1968

Kolodin, Irving. *Music to my Ears : Mitropoulos Returns to the Metropolis*
New York, Saturday Review, October 27, 1951

Kolodin, Irving. *The Guide to Long Playing Records (Orchestral Music)* New York, Alfred A. Knopf 1955

Kutsch,K. J./Riemens, Leo. *Grosses Sängerlexikon* Erstes Band A-L, Zweiter Band M-Z. A. Francke AG.
Verlag Bern 1987

Myers, Kurtz & Hill Richard S. *Record Ratings* New York, Crown Publishers Inc. 1956

Pâris, Alain. *Dictionnaire des Interprètes et de l' Interprétation Musicale au XXe Siècle*
        Première réimpression: Édition revisée 1985
        Paris, Robert Laffont 1985

Rosenthal, Harold & Warrack, John. *The Concise Oxford Dictionary of Opera*
        London, Oxford University Press 1978

Schwann Long Playing Record Catalog Boston, Mass.

Sears, Richard S. *V-Discs, A History & Discography*
        Volume I Greenwood Press, Westport, Conn. 1980
        Volume II Greenwood Press, Westport, Conn. 1986

Seeger, Horst. *Opern Lexikon* Florian Nötzel Verlag «Heinrichshofen Bücher» Wilhelmshaven 1987

The Gramophone Shop Encyclopedia of Recorded Music
        New York, Simon & Schuster 1942 Edition

New York, Simon & Schuster 1948 Edition

The Larousse Encyclopedia of Music
        Edited by Geoffrey Hindley 10th Edition
        The Hamlyn Publishing Group Ltd
        Astronaut House Feltham Middlesex, England 1981

Thomas Tony & Solomon Aubrey. *The Films of 20th Century-Fox*
        Citadel Press, a division of Lyle Stuart Inc.
120 Enterprise Avenue, Secaucus, N.J. 1985

Westrup Jack & Harrison Frank Ll. *Collins Encyclopedia of Music*
        Revised in 1976 by Conrad Wilson,
        Chancellor Press London, 1984 Edition.
        Reprinted 1985 in Czechoslovakia

Greek / Ελληνικές

Δημήτρης Μητρόπουλος, *Η Αλληλογραφία του με την Καίτη Κατσογιάννη*
        Αθήναι, Ίκαρος Δεκέμβριος 1966

Κώστιος Απόστολος. *Δημήτρης Μητρόπουλος* Αθήναι Μορφωτικό Ίδρυμα Εθνικής Τραπέζης 1985

Τσουγιόπουλος Γεώργιος Σ. *Δισκογραφία Δημήτρη Μητρόπουλου* Αθήναι Νέα Εστία Τόμος 70 ος Έτος ΛΕ
        Τεύχος 824 1 Νοεμβρίου 1961

Χριστοπούλου Μαρία. *Δημήτρης Μητρόπουλος Ζωή καί Έργο* Αθήναι 1971

Ωδείον Αθηνών *Δέκατη Εβδόμη Λεπτομερής Έκθεσις των κατά το Σχολικόν Έτος 1912-1913*
        Αθήναι, Π. Δ. Σακελλαρίου 1913

Ωδείον Αθηνών *Τριακοστή Λεπτομερής Έκθεσις Σχολικού Έτους 1925-1926*
        Αθήναι, Εταιρεία «Π. Δ. Σακελλάριος» 1926

Ωδείον Αθηνών *Τριακοστή Τετάρτη Λεπτομερής Έκθεσις Σχολικού Έτους 1929-1930*
    Αθήναι, Εταιρεία «Π. Δ. Σακελλάριος» 1930

Ωδείον Αθηνών *Τριακοστή Πέμπτη Λεπτομερής Έκθεσις Σχολικού Έτους 1930-1931*
    Αθήναι, Εταιρεία «Π. Δ. Σακελλάριος» 1931

Ωδείον Αθηνών *Τεσσαρακοστή Τρίτη Λεπτομερής Έκθεσις Σχολικού Έτους 1938-1939*
    Αθήναι, Πυρσός Α.Ε. 1939

Record Catalogues / Κατάλογοι Δίσκων

Catalogo Generale Dischi Cetra 1963

CBS Masterworks Complete Catalogue Compact Discs 1989/90

Cetra Opera Live 1978-1979-1980

Discocorp. Inc. 1983

Ed Rosen Records

Estro Armonico

Fonit Cetra Catalogo Generale Musica Classica 1983

Foyer Live Recording Catalogue 1984-1985

Giuseppe di Stefano Records

Great Opera Performances Catalogo Generale

Historical Opera Performances Edition

Hunt Productions Compact Disc Catalogo Generale Musica Classica

Melodram 1984

Morgan Records

Movimento Musica 1984

Nuova Era 1988, 1989

Replica Export Catalogue

Unique Opera Record Company (Edward J. Smith Records)

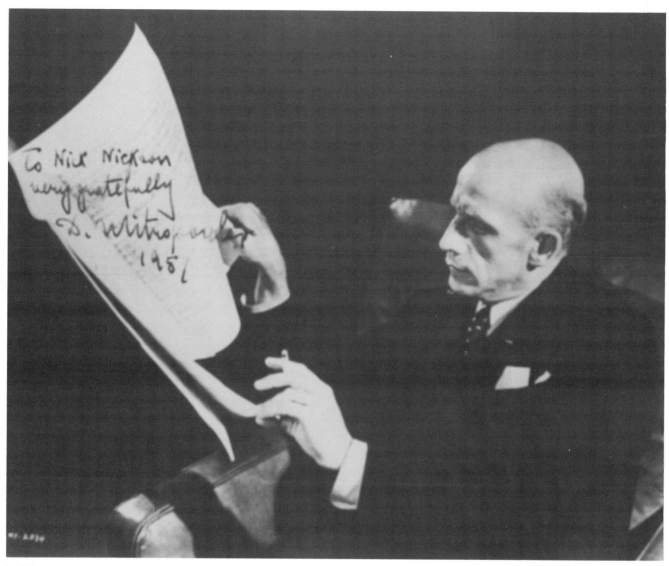

D. Mitropoulos. Photo New York Philharmonic, signed 1957.
(coll. Nick Nickson)

APPENDIX B / ΠΑΡΑΡΤΗΜΑ B

The following notes refer to the corresponding numbers in the discography. The source of information is indicated in parentheses, where applicable.

Οι παρακάτω σημειώσεις αναφέρονται στους αντίστοιχους αριθμούς της δισκογραφίας. Όπου απαιτείται, οι πηγές των πληροφοριών αναφέρονται σε παρένθεση.

1. – Alfredo Casella (1883-1947). Italian composer and pianist.
   – Alfredo Casella (1883-1947). Ιταλός συνθέτης και πιανίστας.

2. – In nos 2, 97, 160, 161 & 162, D. Mitropoulos is performing in the dual capacity of pianist-conductor.
   – Στα υπ' αριθμ. 2, 97, 160, 161 και 162, ο Δ. Μητρόπουλος εμφανίζεται με τη διπλή ιδιότητα του πιανίστα-αρχιμουσικού.

6. – Transcription composed by D. Mitropoulos in 1928 (AK p. 46) or 1929 (KK p. 17)
   – This is his only composition ever recorded under his personal direction.
   – Τη μεταγραφή αυτή ο Δ. Μητρόπουλος συνέθεσε το 1928 (AK. σελ. 46) ή το 1929 (KK σελ . 17)
   – Είναι η μοναδική σύνθεσή του που ηχογραφήθηκε σε δίσκο υπό τη διεύθυνσή του.

7. – Leó Weiner (1885-1960). Notable Hungarian composer and teacher.
   – Leó Weiner (1885-1960). Σημαντικός Ούγγρος συνθέτης και παιδαγωγός.

8. – On the record label, the name of the composer of this transcription is mentioned as Bössenroth, with no initials.
   – In the programme of the Athens Odeon Symphony Orchestra concert of Wednesday July 19, 1939, conducted by D. Mitropoulos, he is mentioned as H. Bösenroth, and this is more likely to be correct. Further data on him were unavailable.

   – Το όνομα του συνθέτη της μεταγραφής αυτής αναφέρεται στην ετικέτα του δίσκου ως Bössenroth, χωρίς μικρό όνομα.
   Στο πρόγραμμα της Συμφωνικής Ορχήστρας του Ωδείου Αθηνών με διευθυντή τον Δ. Μητρόπουλο, της Τετάρτης 19 Ιουλίου 1939, αναφέρεται ως H. Bösenroth, που θα πρέπει να είναι και το σωστό. Περισσότερα στοιχεία γι' αυτόν δεν βρέθηκαν.

9. – World premiere performance was conducted by D. Mitropoulos at the Metropolitan Opera of New York, on January 15, 1958
   – Ο Δ. Μητρόπουλος διηύθυνε την 1η παγκόσμια εκτέλεση στην Μετροπόλιταν Όπερα της Νέας Υόρκης, στις 15 Ιανουαρίου του 1958

16. – The recording date, "February 9, 1956", mentioned on this record is incorrect (see note no 17).
   – A performance with Z. Francescatti on October 26, 1952 was broadcast and taped, and this must be the correct date of recording.
   – Η ημερομηνία 9 Φεβρουαρίου 1956 που αναφέρεται στο δίσκο είναι λανθασμένη (βλ. σημείωση αρ. 17).
   – Η εκτέλεση του έργου αυτού με τον Z. Francescatti, έγινε στις 26 Οκτωβρίου 1952 και υπάρχει σε μαγνητοταινία ραδιοφωνικής μετάδοσης, απ' όπου πρέπει να προέρχεται ο δίσκος αυτός.

17. – The recording date, "February 9, 1956", mentioned on Melodram MEL 210, is incorrect. This performance is identical with those on Mov. Musica 01.005 and Arioso Historical 15.001, both of which derive from a taped radio broadcast of the concert given on February 12, 1956.

   – Η ημερομηνία ηχογράφησης 9 Φεβρουαρίου 1956 που αναφέρεται στο Melodram MEL 210 ειναι λανθασμένη, αφού πρόκειται γιά την ίδια ακριβώς εκτέλεση με τα Mov. Musica 01.005 και Arioso Historical 15.001 τα οποία με τη σειρά τους προέρχονται από τη μαγνητοταινία της ραδιοφωνικής αναμετάδοσης της συναυλίας της 12 Φεβρουαρίου 1956.

22. – The dates "October 15, 1951" and "November 25, 1951", mentioned on Melodram MEL 233 and Melodram CD 18030 respectively, are not correct. This is the same performance as the one on AS Disc CD AS 517 which in turn derives from the taped radio broadcast of the concert given on January 31,1954.

– Οι ημερομηνίες 15 Οκτωβρίου και 25 Νοεμβρίου 1951 που αναφέρονται αντίστοιχα στα Melodram MEL 233 και Melodram CD 18030 ελέγχονται ως ανακριβείς, αφού πρόκειται γιά την ίδια ακριβώς εκτέλεση μέ το AS Disc CD AS 517, το οποίο με τη σειρά του προέρχεται απο τη μαγνητοταινία της ραδιοφωνικής μετάδοσης της συναυλίας της 31 Ιανουαρίου 1954.

25. – The "Angel", referred to in the dedication, was Manon Gropius (1916-1935), who died of polio at a tender age.
She was the daughter of Alma Mahler (1879-1964), widow of the composer, and the famous architect Walter Gropius (1883-1969).
– This concerto was commissioned in 1934 by the American violinist Louis Krassner (1903-   ), who gave its world premiere in Barcelona, Spain, on April 19, 1936.

– Ο «Άγγελος» της αφιέρωσης, ήταν η Manon Gropius (1916-1935), που πέθανε σε τρυφερή ηλικία από πολιομυελίτιδα.
Ήταν η κόρη της Alma Mahler (1879-1964), χήρας του συνθέτη και του διάσημου αρχιτέκτονα Walter Gropius (1883-1969).
– Το κοντσέρτο αυτό παράγγειλε το 1934, ο Αμερικανός βιολιστής Louis Krassner (1903-   ) και το έπαιξε σε πρώτη παγκόσμια εκτέλεση στη Βαρκελώνη, στις 19 Απριλίου 1936.

55. – Yves Chardon (1902-   ),French cellist, member of the Boston Symphony Orchestra, then first cello and associate conductor of the Minneapolis Symphony Orchestra. During the Academic year 1925-1926, he taught the cello class and was a member of the Athens Odeon string quartet which also included Frederic Voloninis, 1st violin, Helen Boustindoui, 2nd violin and Margarita Volonini-Maché, viola.

– Yves Chardon (1902-   ), Γάλλος βιολοντσελλίστας, μέλος της Συμφωνικής Ορχήστρας της Βοστώνης και κατόπιν 1ο βιολοντσέλλο και αναπληρωτής διευθυντής ορχήστρας της Συμφωνικής της Μιννεαπόλεως. Κατά την διάρκεια του σχολικού έτους 1925-1926, εδίδαξε την τάξη του βιολοντσέλλου και υπήρξε μέλος του κουαρτέττου εγχόρδων του Ωδείου Αθηνών μαζύ με τους Φρειδερίκο Βολωνίνη, 1ο βιολί, Ελένη Μπουστίντουϊ, 2ο βιολί και Μαργαρίτα Βολωνίνη-Maché, βιόλα.

58. – Dimitri Rogal–Lewitzsky (-   ). Russian composer and teacher.
– The "Chopiniana" is dedicated to D. Mitropoulos.

– Dimitri Rogal-Lewitzsky (-   ). Ρώσσος συνθέτης και παιδαγωγός.
– Το έργο "Chopiniana" είναι αφιερωμένο στο Δ. Μητρόπουλο.

81. – Composed specially for D. Mitropoulos who conducted the world premiere performance with the New York Philharmonic-Symphony Orchestra on November 16, 1948.(AK. p.86)

– Γραμμένο ειδικά για τον Δ. Μητρόπουλο που διηύθυνε την 1η παγκοσμια εκτέλεση με την Φιλαρμονική-Συμφωνική Ορχήστρα της Νέας Υόρκης, στις 16 Νοεμβρίου 1948 (AK. σελ.86)

85. – Bernardino Molinari (1880-1952), famous Italian conductor.

– Bernardino Molinari (1880-1952), διάσημος Ιταλός διευθυντής ορχήστρας.

89. – Apart from no 106, this is the only other recorded sample of D. Mitropoulos's participation in chamber music performances.

– Μαζί με το υπ' αριθ. 106, τα μόνα δείγματα συμμετοχής του Δ. Μητρόπουλου σε εκτελέσεις έργων μουσικής δωματίου.

94. – D. Mitropoulos conducted the New York Philharmonic-Symphony Orchestra in the world premiere with the composer as soloist.

– Ο Δ. Μητρόπουλος διηύθυνε την 1η παγκόσμια εκτέλεση μέ την Φιλαρμονική-Συμφωνική Ορχήστρα της Νέας Υόρκης και σολίστ τον συνθέτη.

97. – Composed specially for D. Mitropoulos, who conducted and played the piano part in the world premiere with the Minneapolis Symphony Orchestra on November 22, 1946 (AK p. 90). See also note no 2.

– Γραμμένο ειδικά για το Δ. Μητρόπουλο που διηύθυνε την 1η παγκόσμια εκτέλεση, παίζοντας συγχρόνως και το μέρος του πιάνου, με τη Συμφωνική Ορχήστρα της Μιννεαπόλεως, στις 22 Νοεμβρίου 1946 (AK σελ. 90). Βλέπε επίσης σημείωση αρ. 2.

98. – World premiere performance with D. Mitropoulos conducting the Academia di Santa Cecilia Orchestra in Rome, May 24, 1950 (AK. p. 94).
– American premiere with D. Mitropoulos conducting the Cleveland Symphony Orchestra in Cleveland, Ohio, December 9, 1950 (AK. p. 95).
– Anton von Webern (1883-1945), Austrian composer who, along with Alban Berg and their teacher Arnold Schönberg, is one of the principal members of the so-called "Second Viennese School".

– 1η παγκόσμια εκτέλεση απο τον Δ. Μητρόπουλο στην Ρώμη με την Ορχήστρα της Ακαδημίας της Αγίας Καικιλίας, στις 24 Μαίου 1950 (AK. σελ.94).
– 1η εκτέλεση στην Αμερική από τον Δ. Μητρόπουλο στο Κλήβελαντ με την Συμφωνική Ορχήστρα της πόλης αυτής στις 9 Δεκεμβρίου 1950 (AK. σελ.95).
– Anton von Webern (1883-1945), Αυστριακός συνθέτης που, μαζύ με τον Alban Berg και τον καθηγητή τους Arnold Schönberg, είναι τα βασικά μέλη της λεγομένης «Δεύτερης Σχολής της Βιέννης».

105. – Ferruccio Busoni (1866-1924). Italian pianist, composer, conductor and teacher.
D. Mitropoulos attended some of his courses in Berlin.

– Ferruccio Busoni (1866-1924). Ιταλός πιανίστας, συνθέτης, διευθυντής ορχήστρας και παιδαγωγός. Ο Δ. Μητρόπουλος παρακολούθησε μερικά από τα μαθήματά του στο Βερολίνο.

106. – See note no 89.

– Βλ. σημείωση αρ. 89.

107. – Felix Mottl (1856-1911), famous Austrian conductor, assistant to Hans Richter during the first performance of Wagner's "Ring" in Bayreuth in 1876.

– Felix Mottl (1856-1911), διάσημος Αυστριακός διευθυντής ορχήστρας, βοηθός του Hans Richter κατά την πρώτη εκτέλεση της Τετραλογίας του Wagner στο Bayreuth το 1876.

111. – In 1960 the New York Philharmonic Orchestra organised a Mahler Festival in New York, to commemorate the 100th anniversary of the composer's birth.
– During this festival, D. Mitropoulos conducted four of Mahler's symphonies, nos 1, 5, 9 and the incomplete no 10. (KK p. 392)
– The above performances were all broadcast and taped. (see also entries nos 115, 119 and 121)

– Το 1960 στη Νεα Υόρκη η Φιλαρμονική Ορχήστρα της πόλης οργάνωσε Φεστιβάλ Mahler για να γιορτάσει τα 100 χρόνια από την γέννηση του συνθέτη.
– Κατά τη διάρκεια του Φεστιβάλ αυτού, ο Δ. Μητρόπουλος διηύθυνε τέσσερις από τις συμφωνίες του Μάλερ, την 1η, 5η, 9η και την ημιτελή 10η (KK σελ. 392)
– Μεταδόθηκαν όλες από το ραδιόφωνο και μαγνητοφωνήθηκαν. (βλ. επίσης λήμματα υπ᾽ αριθ. 115, 119 και 121).

113. – The date October 24, 1960 mentioned on Cetra DOC 4 is incorrect as, during that concert, Mahler's 3rd symphony was not performed. (Programme of that night's concert in A. Kostios archive).

– Besides this, the performance is identical with those on Rococo 2055 and Mov. Musica 02.016, which in turn derive from the radio broadcast of the concert given on October 31, 1960.

– This was the very last public appearance of the maestro. Two days later, in Milan, he suffered a fatal heart attack while rehearsing the second movement (Tempo di menuetto-Sehr mässig) of this same symphony with the Teatro alla Scala Orchestra.

– Η ημερομηνία 24 Οκτωβρίου 1960, που αναφέρεται στο Cetra DOC 4 είναι λανθασμένη αφού στή συναυλία αυτή δεν παίχτηκε η 3η συμφωνία του Mahler. (Πρόγραμμα στο αρχείον Απ. Κώστιου).

– Εκτος απ' αυτό πρόκειται για την ίδια ακριβώς εκτέλεση με τα Rococo 2055 και Mov. Musica 02.016 που με τη σειρά τους προέρχονται απο την ραδιοφωνική μετάδοση της συναυλίας της 31 Οκτωβρίου 1960.

– Αυτή ήταν η τελευταία εμφάνιση του Δ. Μητρόπουλου μπροστά στο κοινό. Δύο μέρες αργότερα, στο Μιλάνο, υπέστη την μοιραία καρδιακή προσβολή κατά τη διάρκεια των δοκιμών του 2ου μέρους της ίδιας συμφωνίας (Tempo di menuetto- Sehr mässsig) με την ορχήστρα του Θεάτρου της Σκάλας του Μιλάνου.

115. – During the "Mahler Festival" in New York (see note no 111) D. Mitropoulos conducted this symphony both on December 31, 1959 and January 2, 1960. (KK.p.392)

– The one on Replica ARPL 32463 is identical with the other three, all of which derive from the taped radio broadcast of the second performance, so the correct date of this recording should be January 2, 1960.

– Κατά την διάρκεια του «Φεστιβάλ Mahler» στη Νέα Υόρκη (βλ. σημείωση αρ. 111), ο Δ. Μητρόπουλος διηύθυνε τη συμφωνία αυτή στις 31 Δεκεμβρίου 1959 και στις 2 Ιανουαρίου 1960 (KK. σελ. 392).

– Η εκτέλεση στο Replica ARPL 32463 είναι όμοια με αυτές που υπάρχουν στούς άλλους δίσκους και προέρχονται απο την μαγνητοταινία της ραδιοφωνικής μετάδοσης της δεύτερης συναυλίας. Η σωστή ημερομηνία επομένως ειναι, γιά την ηχογράφηση αυτή, η 2 Ιανουαρίου 1960.

116. – D. Mitropoulos conducted the American premiere of this symphony in New York with the Philharmonic-Symphony Orchestra on December 11, 1947 (AK p. 84).

– The dates April 7 and 8, 1955 that are mentioned on Replica ARPL 32463 and Cetra DOC 43 respectively, should be considered erroneous, as the radio transmission took place and was taped on April 10, 1955.

– Ο Δ. Μητρόπουλος διηύθυνε την 1η εκτέλεση της συμφωνίας αυτής στην Αμερική στις 11 Δεκεμβρίου 1947 με την Φιλαρμονική-Συμφωνική Ορχήστρα της Νέας Υόρκης. (AK σελ. 84).

– Οι ημερομηνίες 7 και 8 Απριλίου 1955, που αναφέρονται αντίστοιχα στο Replica ARPL 32463 και το Cetra DOC 43, πρέπει να θεωρηθούν λανθασμένες αφού η ραδιοφωνικη μετάδοση εγινε και ηχογραφήθηκε σε μαγνητοταινία στις 10 Απριλίου 1955.

119. – The date February 12, 1960, mentioned on Mov. Musica 02.026 is incorrect, as this symphony was not performed on that date (KK. p.392).

– This recording is identical with the rest, all of which come from the same taped radio broadcast of January 23, 1960.

– Η ημερομηνία 12 Φεβρουαρίου 1960 που αναφέρεται στο Mov. Musica 02.026 είναι λανθασμένη, αφού η συμφωνία αυτή δεν παίχτηκε εκείνη την ημέρα (KK. σελ 392).

– Πρόκειται για την ίδια εκτέλεση με τους υπόλοιπους δίσκους που προέρχονται όλοι απο την μαγνητοταινία της ραδιοφωνικής μετάδοσης της 23 Ιανουαρίου 1960.

121. – The recording date January 23, 1960, mentioned on Replica RPL 2460/61 is incorrect, as the 9th and not the 10th symphony was performed during that concert. (KK.p.392)

– The date January 17, 1960 which is mentioned on the other records may also be incorrect, because most probably, they all come from the existing taped radio broadcast of January 16, 1960.

– Η ημερομηνία 23 Ιανουαρίου 1960 που αναφέρεται στο Replica RPL 2460/61 είναι λανθασμένη αφού την ημέρα αυτή δεν παίχτηκε η 10η συμφωνία αλλά η 9η (KK. σελ. 392)

– Η ημερομηνία 17 Ιανουαρίου 1960 που αναφέρεται στούς υπόλοιπους δίσκους ελέγχεται ως ανακριβής, γιατί, κατά πάσα πιθανότητα, όλοι προέρχονται απο την υπάρχουσα μαγνητοταινία ραδιοφωνικής μετάδοσης της 16 Ιανουαρίου 1960

135. – The recording date, July 1957, mentioned on Virtuoso CD 2697032 is incorrect. This is the same performance as the one on Val. Records GCL 33, which derives from the taped radio broadcast of the concert given on September 24, 1960 in Cologne, Germany.

– Η ημερομηνία Ιούλιος 1957 που αναφέρεται στο Virtuoso CD 2697032 είναι λανθασμένη αφού πρόκειται για την ίδια εκτέλεση που υπάρχει στο Val. Records GCL 33 και προέρχεται από μαγνητοφώνηση της συναυλίας πού δόθηκε στις 24 Οκτωβρίου 1960 στην Κολωνία.

149. – When the CD HUNT 552 first appeared in 1988, it contained a performance of Don Giovanni which was erroneously attributed to D. Mitropoulos. In fact it contained a Herbert von Karajan performance in Salzburg, in August 1960 with a different cast of singers. The record was subsequently withdrawn, the correct performance was recorded, and in 1990 it was finally released under the SAME record number.

΄Οταν το CD HUNT 552 κυκλοφόρησε αρχικά το 1988, περιείχε μία εκτέλεση του Don Giovanni που λανθασμένα απεδόθη στον Δ. Μητρόπουλο. Στην πραγματικότητα διηύθυνε ο Herbert von Karajan σε μία παράσταση που δόθηκε στο Salzburg τον Αύγουστο του 1960 με διαφορετική διανομή τραγουδιστών. Ο δίσκος αργότερα απεσύρθη, η σωστή εκτέλεση ηχογραφήθηκε, και το 1990 κυκλοφόρησε τελικά με τον ΙΔΙΟ αριθμό δίσκου.

150. – See note no 105.

– Βλέπε σημείωση αρ. 105.

160. – See note no 2.

– Βλέπε σημείωση αρ. 2.

161. – See note no 2.

– Βλέπε σημείωση αρ. 2.

162. – See note no 2.

– Βλέπε σημείωση αρ. 2.

181. – On December 8, 1955, Salvatore Baccaloni sung the role of Sacristan (entry no 180) while on January 7, 1956 this same role was sung by Fernando Corena. Both performances were broadcast and taped.
– Cetra DOC 7 & RDP RDIS 132-9/10 state that these are recordings of the December 8, 1955 performance, but the voice of Fernando Corena is unmistakably heard in both. Therefore, the correct date of recording for the above mentioned records should be January 7, 1956.

– Στις 8 Δεκεμβρίου 1955, τον ρόλο του Νεωκόρου τραγούδησε ο Salvatore Baccaloni (λήμμα 180) ενώ στίς 7 Ιανουαρίου 1956, τον ίδιο ρόλο ερμήνευσε ο Fernando Corena. Και οι δύο αυτές εκτελέσεις μεταδόθηκαν απο το ραδιόφωνο και μαγνητοφωνήθηκαν.
– Τα Cetra DOC 7 & RDP RDIS 132-9/10 αναφέρουν οτι περιέχουν την εκτέλεση της 8 Δεκεμβρίου 1955 αλλά και στα δύο ακούγεται, χωρίς καμιά αμφιβολία, η φωνή του Fernando Corena να τραγουδά τον ρόλο αυτό. Επομένως και οι δύο αυτοί δίσκοι περιέχουν την εκτέλεση της 7 Ιανουαρίου 1956.

190. – See note no 55.

– Βλέπε σημείωση αρ. 55.

204. – Arnold Schönberg's concerto was commissioned by the violinist Louis Krassner, who gave its world premiere on December 6, 1940 with the Philadelphia Symphony Orchestra under Leopold Stokowski (see also note no 25).

– Το κοντσέρτο για βιολί και ορχήστρα του Arnold Schönberg γράφτηκε μετά από παραγγελία του βιολιστή Louis Krassner, που το έπαιξε για πρώτη φορά στις 6 Δεκεμβρίου του 1940 με την Συμφωνική Ορχήστρα της Φιλαδέλφειας και διευθυντή τον Leopold Stokowski (βλ. επίσης σημείωση αρ. 25).

209. – D. Mitropoulos' first LP record (KK. p. 200)

– Ο πρώτος δίσκος Μακράς Διαρκείας του Δ. Μητρόπουλου (ΚΚ. σελ. 200)

ΣΧΟΛΗ ΕΙΔΙΚΩΝ ΘΕΩΡΗΤΙΚΩΝ ΜΑΘΗΜΑΤΩΝ

ΑΡΜΟΝΙΑ

ΤΑΞΙΣ ΠΡΩΤΗ

Αὔξων ἀριθμός	Ὀνοματεπώνυμον	Τόπος γεννήσεως	Διδάσκοντες	Ἔτος σπουδ.
1	Δανασῆ Σοφία	Ἀθῆναι	Καλομοίρης	1
2	Φαραντάτου Μαρία	»	»	1
3	Τσιλιμίγκρα Μαρία	»	»	1
4	Κουρῆ Ἀλεξάνδρα	»	»	1
5	Καζαντζῆ Μαρία	»	»	1
6	Παπαϊωάννου Μαρία	Λεβάδεια	»	1
7	Ἀλεξάνδρου Ἑλένη	Πάτραι	»	1
8	Ἰωαννίδου Ἑλένη	Ἀθῆναι	»	1
9	Παπαδημητρίου Ἀχιλλεὺς	Πάτραι	»	1
10	Σεΐδας Ἰούλιος	Ἀθῆναι	»	1
11	Κολοκωτσᾶς Ἱερώνυμος	Ζάκυνθος	»	1
12	Ἀλβέρτης Ἀλέξανδρος	Σμύρνη	»	1
13	Σκόκος Ἀντώνιος	Ἀθῆναι	»	1
14	Εὐστρατιάδης Ἀλέξανδρος	»	»	1
15	Μητρόπουλος Δημ.	»	Marsick	1

First year students of the Harmony Class of the Athens Odeon. D. Mitropoulos (no 15) was tutored by
A. Marsick.
(coll. S.A. Arfanis)

212. – Composer Gunther Schuller plays fourth horn in this recording.

– Ο συνθέτης Gunther Schuller παίζει το μέρος του τέταρτου κόρνου στην ηχογράφηση αυτή.

222. – On the CD AS Disc AS 543, this composition is erroneously attributed to Robert Sherwood. Research carried out by Nick Nickson in the archive of the New York Philharmonic Orchestra's programmes, proved that the composer of this piece is Gordon Sherwood, born in 1929, Evanston, Illinois.

– Στο κουτί του CD AS Disc AS 543 η σύνθεση αυτή αποδίδεται λανθασμένα στον Robert Sherwood. Μετά από έρευνα που έκανε ο Nick Nickson στο αρχείο προγραμμάτων της Φιλαρμονικής Ορχήστρας της Νέας Υόρκης, απεδείχθη ότι το έργο αυτό είναι του Αμερικανού συνθέτη Gordon Sherwood που γεννήθηκε στο Evanston της πολιτείας Illinois το 1929.

226. – D. Mitropoulos conducted the American premiere of this symphony in New York on October 1954, with the Philharmonic-Symphony Orchestra.

– Ο Δ. Μητρόπουλος διηύθυνε την 1η εκτέλεση της συμφωνίας αυτής στην Αμερική τον Οκτώβριο του 1954, με την Φιλαρμονική-Συμφωνική Ορχήστρα της Νέας Υόρκης.

227. – Composed in 1955/56 (information given by musicologist G. Leotsakos) and dedicated to D. Mitropoulos. – This composition, the "Four Greek Dances" by N. Skalkottas (entry no 229) and "Christus Symphony" by Harilaos Perpessas (1907-   ) (see Appendix E), are the only samples of Greek music recorded under the direction of D. Mitropoulos.

– Γράφτηκε το 1955/56 (πληροφ. Γ. Λεωτσάκος) και αφιερώθηκε στον Δ. Μητρόπουλο.
– Μαζί με τους 4 ελληνικούς χορούς του Σκαλκώτα (λήμμα 229) και την «Συμφωνία του Χριστού» του Χαρίλαου Περπέσα (1907-   ) (βλ. Παράρτημα Ε), είναι τα μόνα Ελληνικά έργα που ηχογραφήθηκαν υπό την διεύθυνση του Δ. Μητρόπουλου.

232. – Guido Cantelli (1920-1956). Famous Italian conductor, killed in an aerorplane crash at Orly, France, on November 24, 1956.

– Guido Cantelli (1920-1956). Διάσημος Ιταλός διευθυντής ορχήστρας που σκοτώθηκε σε αεροπορικό δυστύχημα στο Orly της Γαλλίας, στις 24 Νοεμβρίου 1956.

APPENDIX C / ΠΑΡΑΡΤΗΜΑ Γ

The recordings of D. Mitropoulos in chronological order.
The numbers in parentheses refer to the numbers in the main list.
(L) denotes a Live (pirate) recording.

Οι ηχογραφήσεις του Δ. Μητρόπουλου σε χρονολογική σειρά.
Οι αριθμοί σε παρένθεση αναφέρονται στους αριθμούς της κυρίως δισκογραφίας.
Το (L) υποδηλώνει ζωντανή (πειρατική) ηχογράφηση.

8 Jan.	1940	C. Franck : Symphony in d minor (75)
10 Jan.	1940	S. Prokofiev : Symphony No 1 Op. 25 «Classical» (171)
10 Jan.	1940	F. Mendelssohn : Scherzo from Octet Op. 20 (131)
10 Jan.	1940	P. I. Tchaikovsky : Symphony No 4 Op. 36 1st Session (257)
10 Jan.	1940	L. v. Beethoven : Coriolan Overture Op. 62 (18)
10 Jan.	1940	L. v. Beethoven : Leonore No 3 Overture Op. 72a (19)

10 Jan.	1940	F. Liszt-F.Busoni : Rhapsodie Espagnole (105)
22 Jan.	1940	P. I. Tchaikovsky : Symphony no 4 Op. 36 2nd Session (257)
22 Jan.	1940	L. v. Beethoven : Symphony no 6 Op. 68 "Pastoral" (23)
4 Nov.	1940	G. Mahler : Symphony no 1 "Titan" (108)
26 Nov.	1940	C. Franck : Symphony in d minor (Partial Remake of 75)
26 Nov.	1940	P. I. Tchaikovsky : Symphony no 4 Op. 36 (Partial Remake of 257)
3 Dec.	1940	R. Schumann : Symphony no 2 Op. 61 (216)
3 Dec.	1940	N. Rimsky-Korsakov : "Bridal Procession" from "The Golden Cockerel" Suite (192)
3 Dec.	1940	J. B. Lully-F. Mottl : Menuet from "Le Temple de la Paix" (107)
3 Dec.	1940	W. A. Mozart : Entr' Acts 1 & 2 from "Thamos King of Egypt" (155)
3 Dec.	1940	E. Grieg : Two Elegiac Melodies Op. 34 (83)
3 Dec.	1940	J. S. Bach-L. Weiner : Toccata Adagio & Fugue BWV 564 1st Session (7)
3 Dec.	1940	A. Dvořák : Slavonic Dances Op. 46 nos 1 & 3 (68)
3 Dec.	1940	P. Dukas : The Sorcerer's Apprentice (66)
4 Dec.	1940	J. S. Bach-L. Weiner : Toccata Adagio & Fugue BWV 564 2nd Session (7)
4 Dec.	1940	F. Mendelssohn : Capriccio Brillant Op. 22 (128)
6 Dec.	1941	F. Mendelssohn : Symphony no 3 Op. 56 "Scotch" (133)
6 Dec.	1941	M. Ravel : "Le Tombeau de Couperin" 1st Session (191)
6 Dec.	1941	F. Chopin : Concerto for Piano no 1 Op. 11 (59)
7 Dec.	1941	M. Ravel : "Le Tombeau de Couperin" 2nd Session (191)
7 Dec.	1941	A. Borodin : Symphony no 2 "Bogatyr" (39)
7 Dec.	1941	R. Glière : Sailor's Dance from "The Red Poppy" Ballet (78)
7 Dec.	1941	E. Chabrier : Marche Joyeuse (54)
7 Dec.	1941	G. Meyerbeer : Coronation March from "Le Prophète" (140)
28 Dec.	1941	W. A. Mozart-F. Busoni : "Idomeneo" Overture KV 366 (150) L
4 Apr.	1942	A. Dvořák : Concerto for Cello Op. 104 [Unpublished] (69)
4 Apr.	1942	J. Brahms : Haydn Variations Op. 56a (49)
6 Apr.	1942	J. S. Bach-D. Mitropoulos : Fantasia & Fugue BWV 542 (6)
6 Apr.	1942	J. S. Bach- H. Bösenroth : "Wir Glauben" Chorale Prelude BWV 680 (8)
6 Apr.	1942	A. Glazunov : Overture on three Greek Themes Op. 3 (77)
6 Apr.	1942	G. F. Händel-B. Molinari : Largo from "Xerxes" [Unpublished] (85)
6 Apr.	1942	J. Massenet : Meditation from "Thais" [Unpublished] (126)
6 Apr.	1942	J. Offenbach : "Orpheus in the Underworld" Overture [Unpublished] (158)
2 Mar.	1945	S. Rachmaninov : "The Isle of the Dead" Op. 29 (186)
2 Mar.	1945	E. Siegmeister : "Ozark Set" (228)
2 Mar.	1945	F. Couperin-D. Milhaud : Overture & Allegro (62)
2 Mar.	1945	E. Lalo : "Le Roi d' Ys" Overture (99)
2 Mar.	1945	M. Ravel-Y. Chardon : Piece en Forme de Habanera (190)
2 Mar.	1945	Y. Chardon : "Rhumba" for Cello & Orchestra (55)
2 Mar.	1945	N. Rimsky-Korsakov : "The Golden Cockerel" Suite (193)

2 Mar.	1945	R. Vaughan-Williams : Fantasia on a Theme by Thomas Tallis (260)
2 Mar.	1945	D. Milhaud :"Le Bœuf sur le Toit" Ballet (141)
21 Sep.	1945	W. A. Mozart : Concerto for Two Pianos no 10 KV 365 (145)
21 Sep.	1945	F. Chopin-D. Rogal-Lewitzsky :" Chopiniana" (58)
7 Oct.	1945	P. Mascagni : "Addio alla Madre" from Cavalleria Rusticana (124) L
9 Dec.	1945	W. A. Mozart : "Magic Flute" Overture KV 620 (151) L
16 Dec.	1945	J. S. Bach : Brandenburg Concerto no 5 BWV 1050 (2) L
16 Dec.	1945	S. Prokofiev : Concerto for Piano no 3 Op. 26 (160) L
30 Dec.	1945	A. Berg : Concerto for Violin "To the Memory of an Angel" (25) L
9 Mar.	1946	E. Chausson : Symphony in B flat Op. 20 (56)
10 Mar.	1946	W. Walton : "Portsmouth Point" Overture (277)
10 Mar.	1946	P. I. Tchaikovsky : Symphony no 2 Op. 17 1st Session (256)
11 Mar.	1946	P. I. Tchaikovsky : Symphony no 2 Op. 17 2nd Session (256)
11 Mar.	1946	C. M. v. Weber : "Jubel" Overture (278)
11 Mar.	1946	J. Massenet : "Scènes Alsaciennes" Suite Op. 7 (125)
26 Jul.	1946	S. Prokofiev : Concerto for Piano no 3 Op. 26 (161)
26 Jul.	1946	P. Mascagni : Intermezzo from "Cavalleria Rusticana" (123)
26 Jul.	1946	G. Puccini : Intermezzo from "Manon Lescaut" (178)
26 Jul.	1946	E. Wolf-Ferrari : Intermezzo from Act 2 of "I Gioielli della Madonna" (282)
26 Jul.	1946	E. Wolf-Ferrari : Intermezzo from Act 3 of "I Gioielli della Madonna" (283)
26 Jul.	1946	G. C. Menotti : "Sebastian" Ballet Suite (139)
19 Jan.	1947	S. Rachmaninov : Symphony no 2 Op. 27 1st movement (187)
20 Jan.	1947	S. Rachmaninov : Symphony no 2 Op. 27 2nd, 3rd & 4th movements (187)
20 Jan.	1947	M. Gould : "Minstrel Show" (82)
20 Jan.	1947	J. Weinberger : Polka & Fugue from "Schwanda the Bagpiper" (280)
20 Jan.	1947	R. Schumann : Symphony no 3 Op. 97 "Rhenish" (217)
16 Nov.	1947	P. I. Tchaikovsky : Concerto for Piano no 1 Op. 23 (250)
15 Dec.	1947	F. Poulenc : Concerto for Two Pianos and Orchestra (159)
24 Oct.	1948	J. Brahms : Concerto for Violin Op. 77 (44) L
21 Nov.	1948	R. Schumann : Concerto for Piano Op. 54 (213) L
9 Aug.	1949	S. Prokofiev : Concerto for Piano no 3 Op. 26 (162) L
11 Dec.	1949	E. Krenek : Concerto for Piano no 3 (97) L
18 Dec.	1949	J. S. Bach : Concerto for Violin BWV 1056 (5) L
18 Dec.	1949	W. A. Mozart : Concerto for Violin no 3 KV 216 (147) L
Dec.	1949	A. Schönberg : Serenade for Septet & Baritone Op. 24 (209)
25 Dec.	1949	R. Strauss : "Electra" Op. 58 Complete (237) L
	1950	S. Prokofiev : Quintet Op. 39 (168)
	1950	S. Prokofiev : Overture on Hebrew Themes Op. 34 (167)
	1950	H. Swanson : "Night Music" (247)

Dimitri Mitropoulos

D. Mitropoulos conducts. Photo X from the album "Ovation". The Minnesota Orchestra's 75th Anniversary.

3 Jan.	1950	A. Khachaturian : Concerto for Piano (93)
15 Jan.	1950	L. v. Beethoven : Concerto for Violin Op. 61 (15) L
16 Jan.	1950	R. Sessions : Symphony no 2 (221)
23 Jan.	1950	M. Gould : "Philharmonic Waltzes" (81)
23 Jan.	1950	C. Saint-Saëns : "Le Rouet d' Omphale" Op. 31 (201)
23 Jan.	1950	H. Rabaud : "La Procession Nocturne" Op. 6 (185)
23 Jan.	1950	C. Saint-Saëns : Concerto for Violin no 3 Op. 61 (197)
23 Apr.	1950	R. Strauss: "Sinfonia Domestica" Op. 53 (244) L
May	1950	G. F. Malipiero : Symphony no 7 "Delle Canzoni" (122)
May	1950	J. S. Bach-A. Casella : "Chaconne" BWV 1004 (1)
16 May	1950	R. Strauss : "Electra" Op. 58 Complete Part 1 (238)
18 May	1950	R. Strauss : "Electra" Op. 58 Complete Part 2 (238)
27 Nov.	1950	C. Debussy : "La Mer" (65)
27 Nov.	1950	C. Saint-Saëns : "Danse Macabre" Op. 40 (198)
27 Nov.	1950	J. S. Bach : Concerto for Three Harpsichords BWV 1063 (4)
4 Mar.	1951	A. Dvořák : Concerto for Violin Op. 53 (70) L
5 Mar.	1951	I. Stravinsky : "Petrouchka" Ballet (246)
12 Apr.	1951	A. Berg : "Wozzeck" Complete Part 1 (26)
13 Apr.	1951	A. Berg : "Wozzeck" Complete Part 2 (26)
15 Apr.	1951	A. Berg : "Wozzeck" Complete Part 3 (26)
21 Apr.	1951	E. Krenek : "Symphonic Elegy" for String Orchestra (98)
21 Apr.	1951	E. Bloch : "Schelomo" Op. 33 (35)
21 Apr.	1951	C. Saint-Saëns : Concerto for Cello no 1 Op. 33 (195)
22 Apr.	1951	A. Bax : Overture to a Picaresque Comedy (11) L
22 Apr.	1951	L. v. Beethoven : Concerto for Piano no 4 Op. 58 (13) L
22 Apr.	1951	W. A. Mozart : Symphony no 39 KV 543 (154) L
14 Oct.	1951	F. Busoni : "Arlecchino" Complete (53) L
21 Oct.	1951	G. Mahler : Symphony no 1 "Titan" (109) L
18 Nov.	1951	A. Schönberg : "Erwartung" Op. 17 (207) L
19 Nov.	1951	A. Schönberg : "Erwartung" Op. 17 (208)
4 Jan.	1952	R. E. Travis : "Symphonic Allegro" (248)
4 Jan.	1952	F. Couperin-D. Milhaud : Overture & Allegro (63)
4 Jan.	1952	M. Bruch : Concerto for Violin no 1 Op. 26 (52)
10 Feb.	1952	R. Schumann : Concerto for Piano Op. 54 (214) L
31 Mar.	1952	A. Rubinstein : Concerto for Piano no 4 Op. 70 (194)
31 Mar.	1952	M. Gould : "Fall River Legend" Ballet Suite (80)
21 Apr.	1952	P. Hindemith : Sonata for Oboe & Piano (89)
21 Apr.	1952	C. M. Löffler : Two Rhapsodies for Oboe, Viola & Piano (106)
26 Oct.	1952	L. v. Beethoven : Concerto for Violin Op. 61 (16) L
27 Oct.	1952	H. Berlioz : "Romeo & Juliet" Symphony Op. 17 Orchestral Parts (30)
27 Oct.	1952	S. Prokofiev : Concerto for Violin no 2 Op. 63 (165)

ΕΘΝΙΚΟΝ ΩΔΕΙΟΝ

ΟΔΟΣ ΚΥΒΕΛΗΣ 3 - ΜΟΥΣΕΙΟΝ ΑΡΙΘ. ΤΗΛΕΦ. 73-41

ΘΕΑΤΡΟΝ ΟΛΥΜΠΙΑ

ΠΑΡΑΣΚΕΥΗ 9 ΙΑΝΟΥΑΡΙΟΥ 1931 ΩΡΑ 10 Μ.Μ. *(ΒΡΑΔΥΝΗ)*
ΚΥΡΙΑΚΗ 11 ΙΑΝΟΥΑΡΙΟΥ 1931 ΩΡΑ 6 Μ.Μ. *(ΑΠΟΓΕΥΜΑΤΙΝΗ)*

ΔΥΟ ΜΟΝΟΝ ΠΑΡΑΣΤΑΣΕΙΣ

ΜΑΝΩΛΗ ΚΑΛΟΜΟΙΡΗ

ΤΟ ΔΑΧΤΥΛΙΔΙ ΤΗΣ ΜΑΝΑΣ

ΜΟΥΣΙΚΟΔΡΑΜΑ ΣΕ ΤΡΕΙΣ ΠΡΑΞΕΙΣ

ΕΠΑΝΩ ΣΤΟ ΟΜΩΝΥΜΟ ΔΡΑΜΑ ΤΟΥ ΓΙΑΝΝΗ ΚΑΜΠΙΣΗ

ΣΤΙΧΟΙ: ΑΓΝΗ ΟΡΦΙΚΟΥ

ΔΙΕΥΘΥΝΤΗΣ ΟΡΧΗΣΤΡΑΣ

ΔΗΜ. ΜΗΤΡΟΠΟΥΛΟΣ

ΣΥΜΠΡΑΞΙΣ: Κᴬ ΜΑΡΙΚΑ ΚΑΛΦΟΠΟΥΛΟΥ
(Καθηγήτρια Ἐθν. Ὠδείου **Soliste** τῶν **Concerts Colonne**)

Δᴵˢ ΚΑΙΤΗ ΑΝΔΡΕΑΔΟΥ
(**Soliste** τῶν **Concerts Colonne et Pasdeloup**)

Κᴼˢ ΠΕΤΡΟΣ ΕΠΙΤΡΟΠΑΚΗΣ
(Τοῦ Ἑλληνικοῦ Μελοδράματος)

Κᴼˢ ΤΖΩΝ ΒΛΑΪΚΟΣ
(α' Βραβεῖον Ἐθνικοῦ Ὠδείου)

Δᴺᴵᵉ Π. ΚΑΠΕΡΩΝΗ Μ. ΠΑΠΑΔΑΤΟΥ — Κᴼˢ ΝΙΚ. ΜΟΣΧΟΝΑΣ
(Τελειόφοιτοι Ἐθνικοῦ Ὠδείου)

ΧΩΡΟΔΙΑ 80 ΠΡΟΣΩΠΩΝ - ΟΡΧΗΣΤΡΑ 60 ΟΡΓΑΝΩΝ

ΜΠΑΛΕΤΤΟ 20 ΠΡΟΣΩΠΩΝ
κατὰ διδασκαλίαν τῆς **Mme Tilde de Vajda**

ΜΟΥΣΙΚΟΣ ΔΙΕΥΘΥΝΤΗΣ ΣΚΗΝΗΣ ΛΕΩΝ. ΖΩΡΑΣ

D. Mitropoulos conducts M. Kalomiris' opera "The Mother's Ring" January 9 & 11, 1931.
(coll. S.A. Arfanis)

1 Dec.	1952	A. Schönberg : Concerto for Violin Op. 36 (204)
1 Dec.	1952	D. Shostakovich : Symphony no 5 Op. 47 (225)
1 Dec.	1952	A. Borodin : Polovtsian Dances from "Prince Igor" (36)
20 Mar.	1953	A. Borodin : "In the Steppes of Central Asia" (37)
20 Mar.	1953	M. Ippolitov-Ivanov : "Caucasian Sketches" Op. 10 (91)
20 Mar.	1953	A. Scriabin : "Poem of Ecstasy" Op. 54 (218)
20 Mar.	1953	A. Scriabin : "Poem of Fire" Op. 60 (220)
12 Apr.	1953	W. A. Mozart : "Le Nozze di Figaro" Overture KV 492 (153) L
12 Apr.	1953	J. Brahms : Concerto for Piano no 1 Op. 15 (42) L
19 Apr.	1953	A. Scriabin : "The Poem of Ecstasy" Op. 54 (219) L
19 Apr.	1953	C. Saint-Saëns : Concerto for Piano no 2 Op. 22 (196) L
19 Apr.	1953	C. Franck : Symphonic Variations for Piano & Orchestra (74) L
19 Apr.	1953	A. Borodin : "In the Steppes of Central Asia" (38) L
26 Apr.	1953	E. Chausson : Symphony in B flat Op. 20 (57) L
14 Jun.	1953	G. Verdi : "La Forza del Destino" Complete (267) L
17 Jun.	1953	G. Verdi : "La Forza del Destino" Overture (268) L
17 Jun.	1953	F. Liszt : Concerto for Piano no 1 (102) L
17 Jun.	1953	W. A. Mozart : Concerto for Piano no 20 KV 466 (143) L
17 Jun.	1953	J. Brahms : Symphony no 3 Op. 90 (46) L
18 Oct.	1953	G. B. Viotti : Concerto for Violin no 22 (271) L
25 Oct.	1953	P. Hindemith : "The Harmony of the World" (90) L
2 Nov.	1953	A. Borodin : Symphony no 2 "Bogatyr" (40)
2 Nov.	1953	M. De Falla : Interlude & Dance from "La Vida Breve" (72)
2 Nov.	1953	M. De Falla : Three Dances from "The Three Cornered Hat" (71)
2 Nov.	1953	F. Mendelssohn : "Ruy Blas" Overture Op.95 (132)
2 Nov.	1953	F. Mendelssohn : "Calm Sea & Prosperous Voyage" Overture Op 27 [Unpublished] (127)
2 Nov.	1953	F. Mendelssohn : "Hebrides" Overture Op. 26 (130)
2 Nov.	1953	F. Mendelssohn : Symphony no 3 Op. 56 "Scotch" (134)
2 Nov.	1953	F. Mendelssohn : Symphony no 5 Op. 107 "Reformation" (136)
8 Nov.	1953	L. v. Beethoven : "Missa Solemnis" Op. 123 (20) L
21 Jan.	1954	H. Berlioz : "Les Nuits d' Été" Song Cycle Op. 7 (27)
25 Jan.	1954	Z. Kodály : Dances from Galanta [Unpublished] (95)
31 Jan.	1954	L. v. Beethoven : Symphony no 1 Op. 21 (22) L
1 Feb.	1954	P. Mennin : Symphony no 3 (138)
7 Feb.	1954	F. J. Haydn : English Opera Overture (86) L
7 Feb.	1954	F. J. Haydn : Symphony no 80 (87) L
7 Feb.	1954	A. Copland : Appalachian Spring Suite (61) L
7 Feb.	1954	C. Debussy : Iberia no 2 from Images (64) L
11 Feb.	1954	R. Strauss: "Die Frau ohne Schatten" Op. 65 Symphonic Fantasy (233) L
21 Feb.	1954	D. Cimarosa : "Beautiful Grecian Overture" (60) L

21 Feb.	1954	L. v Beethoven : Prometheus Ballet Music Op. 43 Excerpts (21) L
27 Mar.	1954	P. I. Tchaikovsky : Concerto for Violin Op. 35 (251)
27 Mar.	1954	P. I. Tchaikovsky : Symphony no 5 Op. 64 (258)
25 Apr.	1954	G. Bizet: Symphony no 1 in C major (34) L
2 May	1954	S. Rachmaninov : Symphony no 2 Op. 27 (188) L
15 Jun.	1954	G. Puccini : "La Fanciulla del West" Complete (174) L
9 Jul.	1954	A.Schönberg : Concerto for Violin Op. 36 (205) L
9 Jul.	1954	S. Prokofiev : Symphony no 5 Op. 100 (172) L
16 Jul.	1954	A. Schönberg : Concerto for Violin Op. 36 (206) L
18 Oct.	1954	D. Shostakovitch : Symphony no 10 Op. 93 (226)
18 Oct.	1954	P. I. Tchaikovsky : Suite no 1 Op. 43 1st Session (255)
17 Nov.	1954	P. I. Tchaikovsky : Suite no 1 Op. 43 2nd Session (255)
17 Nov.	1954	F. Mendelssohn : Concerto for Violin Op. 64 (129)
8 Jan.	1955	R. Strauss : "Salome" Op. 54 Complete (241) L
9 Jan.	1955	G. Verdi : "Un Ballo in Maschera" Abridged 1st Session Act 1 (263)
21 Jan.	1955	G. Verdi : "Un Ballo in Maschera" Abridged 2nd Session Acts 2 & 3 (263)
22 Jan.	1955	G. Verdi : "Un Ballo in Maschera" Complete (264) L
13 Feb.	1955	J. Brahms : Haydn Variations Op. 56a (50) L
13 Feb.	1955	J. Brahms : Concerto for Piano no 1 Op. 15 (43) L
27 Feb.	1955	S. Prokofiev : Scythian Suite Op. 20 (170) L
10 Apr.	1955	G. Mahler : Symphony no 6 "Tragic" (116) L
8 May	1955	J. Brahms : Haydn Variations Op. 56a (51) L
8 May	1955	S. Prokofiev : Symphony no 5 Op. 100 (173) L
8 May	1955	S. Rachmaninov : "Vocalise" Op. 34 (189) L
28 May.	1955	G. Mahler : Symphony no 5 (114) L
15 Jun.	1955	G. Mahler : Symphony no 1 "Titan" (110) L
15 Jun.	1955	G. Mahler : Symphony no 10 "Adagio" (120) L
19 Sep.	1955	L. v. Beethoven : Concerto for Piano no 5 Op. 73 "Emperor" (14)
23 Oct.	1955	W. A. Mozart : Concerto for Piano no 16 KV 451 (142) L
23 Oct.	1955	W. A. Mozart : Concerto for Piano no 25 KV 503 (144) L
30 Oct.	1955	R. Wagner : "Götterdämmerung" Act 3 Complete (275) L
30 Oct.	1955	R. Wagner : Forest Murmurs from Act 2 of "Siegfried" (276) L
13 Nov.	1955	W. A. Mozart : Concerto for Two Pianos no 10 KV 365 (146) L
8 Dec.	1955	G. Puccini : "Tosca" Complete (180) L
1 Jan.	1956	W. A. Mozart : Concerto for Violin no 5 KV 219 "Turkish" (148) L
1 Jan.	1956	D. Shostakovitch : Concerto for Violin no 1 Op 99 (223) L
2 Jan.	1956	D. Shostakovitch : Concerto for Violin no 1 Op. 99 (224)
6 Jan.	1956	C. Saint-Saëns : "La Jeunesse d' Hercule" Op. 50 (199)
7 Jan.	1956	G. Puccini : "Tosca" Complete (181) L
9 Jan.	1956	S. Prokofiev : "Lieutenant Kije" Suite Op. 60 (166)

9 Jan.	1956	C. Saint-Saëns : "Phaeton" Op. 39 (200)
9 Jan.	1956	N. Skalkottas : Four Greek Dances (229)
9 Jan.	1956	R. Vaughan-Williams : Symphony no 4 (262)
12 Feb.	1956	L. v. Beethoven : Concerto for Violin Op. 61 (17) L
24 Feb.	1956	L. Kirchner : Concerto for Piano (94)
24 Feb.	1956	F. Liszt : "Les Préludes" [Unpublished] (103)
26 Feb.	1956	M. I. Glinka : "Russlan & Ludmilla" Overture (79) L
26 Feb.	1956	S. Prokofiev : Concerto for Violin no 1 Op. 19 (163) L
27 Feb.	1956	F. Liszt : "Les Préludes" (104)
27 Feb.	1956	Z. Kodály : "Hary Janos" Suite (96)
27 Feb.	1956	S. Prokofiev : Concerto for Violin no 1 Op. 19 (164)
Mar.	1956	M. Mussorgsky : "Boris Godunov" Abridged (156)
31 Mar.	1956	G. Puccini : "Manon Lescaut" Complete (179) L
15 Apr.	1956	G. Mahler : Symphony no 3 in d minor (112) L
14 Jun.	1956	G.Schuller : Symphony for Brass & Percussion Op. 16 (212)
24 Jul.	1956	W. A. Mozart : "Don Giovanni" KV 527 Complete (149) L
15 Aug.	1956	H. Berlioz : Requiem Op. 5 (28) L
26 Aug.	1956	H. Berlioz : Requiem Op. 5 (29) L
19 Sep.	1956	R. Strauss : "Eine Alpensinfonie" Op. 64 (236) L
26 Oct.	1956	R, Strauss : "Don Juan" Op. 20 (234) L
28 Oct.	1956	J. Brahms : Symphony no 4 Op. 98 (48) L
2 Nov.	1956	M. De Falla : "Nights in the Gardens of Spain" (73)
2 Nov.	1956	P. Dukas : "The Sorcerer's Apprentice" (67)
2 Nov.	1956	J. Weinberger : Polka & Fugue from "Schwanda the Bagpiper" (281)
3 Nov.	1956	R. Strauss : Dance of the Seven Veils from "Salome" Op. 54 (242)
4 Nov.	1956	F. J. Haydn : Symphony no 100 "Military" (88) L
11 Nov.	1956	R. Schumann : Symphony no 1 Op. 38 "Spring" (215) L
25 Nov.	1956	G. Puccini : Duet Tosca-Scarpia from Act 2 of "Tosca" (182) L
2 Dec.	1956	R. Strauss : "Tod und Verklärung" Op. 24 (232) L
15 Dec.	1956	G. Puccini : "Madama Butterfly" Complete (175) L
29 Dec.	1956	G. Verdi : "Ernani" Complete (265) L
Jan.	1957	G. Puccini : "Madama Butterfly" Abridged (176)
12 Jan.	1957	G. Bizet : "Carmen" Complete (33) L
2 Feb.	1957	R. Wagner : "Die Walküre" Complete (272) L
Feb.	1957	R. Wagner : "Die Walküre" Scenes (273)
20 Feb.	1957	R. Wagner : Wotan's Farewell & Magic Fire Music from "Die Walküre" (274) L
23 Feb.	1957	L. v. Beethoven : Concerto for Piano no 3 Op. 37 (12)
24 Feb.	1957	A. Ginastera : Overture to the "Creole Faust" (76) L
24 Feb.	1957	H. Berlioz : Symphonie Fantastique Op. 14 (31)
Mar.	1957	G. Puccini : "Tosca" Complete (183)

21 Mar.	1957	M. De Falla : Nights in the Gardens of Spain (Harp Dubbing) (73)
14 Apr.	1957	H. Berlioz : Symphonie Fantastique Op. 14 (32) L
22 Apr.	1957	E. Lalo : "Symphonie Espagnole" for Violin Op. 21 (100)
22 Apr.	1957	P. I. Tchaikovsky : "Capriccio Italien" Op. 45 (249)
5 May	1957	G. Sherwood : Introduction & Allegro (222) L
5 May	1957	L. v Beethoven : Symphony no 8 Op. 93 (24) L
14 Jun.	1957	G. Verdi : "Ernani" Complete (266) L
19 Jul.	1957	F. Mendelssohn : Symphony no 5 Op. 107 "Reformation" (137) L
19 Jul.	1957	R. Strauss : "Sinfonia Domestica" Op. 53 (245) L
7 Aug.	1957	R. Strauss : "Electra" Op. 58 Complete (239) L
11 Nov.	1957	F. S. Key : "The Star Spangled Banner" [Unpublished] (92)
11 Nov.	1957	M. Mussorgsky : "Night on Bald Mountain" (157)
11 Nov.	1957	S. Prokofiev : "Romeo & Juliet" Excerpts from the Ballet (169)
11 Nov.	1957	P. I. Tchaikovsky : "Marche Slave" Op. 31 (254)
11 Nov.	1957	P. I. Tchaikovsky : Symphony no 6 Op. 74 "Pathétique" (259)
7 Dec.	1957	P. I. Tchaikovsky : "Eugen Oniegin" Complete (252) L
Dec.	1957	P. I. Tchaikovsky : "Eugen Oniegin" Abridged (253)
2 Feb.	1958	W. A. Mozart : "Magic Flute" Overture KV 620 (152) L
8 Feb.	1958	R. Strauss : "Salome" Op. 54 Complete (243) L
9 Feb.	1958	J. Brahms : "Academic Festival" Overture Op. 80 (41) L
9 Feb.	1958	J. Brahms : Symphony no 3 Op. 90 (47) L
9 Feb.	1958	R. Strauss : "Burleske" for Piano and Orchestra (231) L
23 Feb.	1958	S. Barber : "Vanessa" Complete 1st Session (9)
1 Mar.	1958	Y. Sicilianos : Symphony no 1 Op. 14 (227) L
3 Mar.	1958	A. Schönberg : "Transfigured Night" Op. 4 (210)
3 Mar.	1958	R. Vaughan-Williams : "Fantasia on a Theme by Thomas Tallis" (261)
16 Mar.	1958	C. Guarnieri : Prologo y Fuga (84) L
16 Mar.	1958	S. Barber : Medea's Meditation & Dance of Vengeance Op. 23a (10) L
3 Apr.	1958	A. Schönberg : Concerto for Piano Op. 42 (203) L
7 Apr.	1958	S. Barber : "Vanessa" Complete 2nd Session (9)
10 Apr.	1958	S. Barber : "Vanessa" Complete 3rd Session (9)
10 Aug.	1958	J. S. Bach : Concerto for Harpsichord no 1 BWV 1052 (3) L
24 Aug.	1958	J. Brahms : Concerto for Violin Op. 77 (45) L
3 Jan.	1959	R. Leoncavallo : "I Pagliacci" Highlights (101) L
23 Aug.	1959	F. Schmidt : "The Book with Seven Seals" Oratorio (202) L
31 Aug.	1959	B. A. Zimmermann : Concerto for Oboe (284) L
31 Aug.	1959	G. Mahler : Symphony no 6 "Tragic" (117) L
7 Sep.	1959	R. Strauss : Electra's Monologue from "Electra" Op. 58 (240) L
7 Sep.	1959	R. Strauss : "Also Sprach Zarathustra" Op. 30 (230) L
7 Sep.	1959	R. Strauss : "Don Quixote" Op. 35 (235) L

ΩΔΕΙΟΝ ΑΘΗΝΩΝ
1871

ΘΕΑΤΡΟΝ ΟΛΥΜΠΙΑ

Πέμπτη 27 Ἀπριλίου 1933, ὥραν 7 μ. μ.

ΡΕΣΙΤΑΛ

ΤΗΣ ΠΑΓΚΟΣΜΙΟΥ ΦΗΜΗΣ ΚΑΛΛΙΤΕΧΝΙΔΟΣ ΤΟΥ ΑΣΜΑΤΟΣ

KAMMERSÄNGERIN

ELISABETH

SCHUMANN

ΤΗΣ ΚΡΑΤΙΚΗΣ ΟΠΕΡΑΣ ΒΕΡΟΛΙΝΟΥ ΚΑΙ ΒΙΕΝΝΗΣ

ΕΙΣ ΤΟ ΠΙΑΝΟ Ο ΚΥΡΙΟΣ

ΔΗΜ. ΜΗΤΡΟΠΟΥΛΟΣ

ΤΙΜΑΙ ΕΙΣΙΤΗΡΙΩΝ

Θεωρεῖον Α΄. Δρχ. 175, Πλατεῖα καὶ Ἀμφιθέατρον Α΄. Δρχ. 150, Ἀμφιθέατρον Β΄. Δρχ. 125, Ἐξώστης Δρχ. 90, Θεωρεῖον Β΄. Δρχ. 75, Ὑπερῷον Δρχ. 50.

Διὰ τοὺς Συνδρομητὰς τῶν Συμφωνικῶν Συναυλιῶν τοῦ Ὠδείου, Θεωρεῖον Α΄. Δρχ. 120, Πλατεῖα καὶ Ἀμφιθέατρον Α΄. Δρχ. 120.

Τὰ εἰσιτήρια πωλοῦνται εἰς τὸ Ταμεῖον τοῦ Ὠδείου Ἀθηνῶν (Ὁδὸς Πειραιῶς τηλ. 25-351) καὶ εἰς τὸ Θέατρον «Ὀλύμπια».

TO ΠΡΟΓΡΑΜΜΑ ΤΙΜΑΤΑΙ 1 ΔΡΑΧΜΗΣ

Elisabeth Schumann's recital at the Olympia Theatre, Athens on April 27, 1930. At the piano D. Mitropoulos. (coll. S. A. Arfanis)

21 Nov.	1959	G. Puccini : "Tosca" Complete (184) L
2 Jan.	1960	G. Mahler : Symphony no 5 (115) L
9 Jan.	1960	G. Mahler : Symphony no 1 "Titan" (111) L
16 Jan.	1960	G. Mahler : Symphony no 10 "Adagio" (121) L
23 Jan.	1960	A. v Webern : Passacaglia for Orchestra Op. 1 (279) L
23 Jan.	1960	G. Mahler : Symphony no 9 (119) L
2 Apr.	1960	G. Verdi : "Simon Boccanegra" Complete (270) L
16 Apr.	1960	G. Puccini : "Madama Butterfly" Complete (177) L
21 Aug.	1960	A. Schönberg : Variations for Orchestra Op. 31 (211) L
28 Aug.	1960	G. Mahler : Symphony no 8 "Symphony of a Thousand" (118) L
23 Sep.	1960	G. Verdi : "La Forza del Destino" Complete (269) L
24 Oct.	1960	F. Mendelssohn : Symphony no 3 Op. 56 "Scotch" (135) L
31 Oct.	1960	G. Mahler : Symphony no 3 in d minor (113) L

APPENDIX D / ΠΑΡΑΡΤΗΜΑ Δ

Index of names of all the artists who have collaborated with, or performed under D. Mitropoulos' direction in recordings.
Ευρετήριο ονομάτων όλων των καλλιτεχνών που συνεργάστηκαν με τον Δημήτρη Μητρόπουλο ή έπαιξαν υπό την διεύθυνσή του σε ηχογραφήσεις δίσκων

ASSISTANT CONDUCTORS / ΒΟΗΘΟΙ ΔΙΕΥΘΥΝΤΕΣ ΟΡΧΗΣΤΡΑΣ

Rich, Martin	183.
Strasfogel, Ignace	9, 156, 253.

CHOIRS / ΧΟΡΩΔΙΕΣ

Chorus of the Friends of Music Vienna	118, 202.
Cologne Radio Chorus	29.
Cologne Radio Women's Chorus	113.
Cologne School Boys' Chorus	113.
High School of Music & Arts Chorus New York	26.
Maggio Musicale Fiorentino Festival Chorus	238.
Metropolitan Opera Chorus	9, 33,101,156, 175, 176, 177, 179, 180, 181, 183, 184, 252, 253, 264, 265, 270.

CHORUS MASTERS / ΔΙΕΥΘΥΝΤΕΣ ΧΟΡΩΔΙΑΣ

INSTRUMENTALISTS / ΣΟΛΙΣΤ ΟΡΓΑΝΩΝ

Baritone – Παραλλαγή ευφωνίου

Bass – Κοντραμπάσο

Bassoon – Φαγκότο

Cello – Βιολοντσέλλο

Clarinet – Κλαρινέτο

ΩΔΕΙΟΝ ΑΘΗΝΩΝ
1871
ΣΥΝΑΥΛΙΑΙ ΤΗΣ ΣΥΜΦΩΝΙΚΗΣ ΟΡΧΗΣΤΡΑΣ

ΘΕΑΤΡΟΝ ΟΛΥΜΠΙΑ

Δευτέρα 18 Νοεμβρίου 1935, ὥραν 6.30΄ μ.μ. ἀκριβῶς

ΣΥΝΑΥΛΙΑ

ΔΕΥΤΕΡΑ ΣΥΝΔΡΟΜΗΤΩΝ

ΤΗΣ

ΣΥΜΦΩΝΙΚΗΣ ΟΡΧΗΣΤΡΑΣ

ΤΟΥ

ΩΔΕΙΟΥ ΑΘΗΝΩΝ

1893 - 1935

ΔΙΕΥΘΥΝΤΗΣ ΟΡΧΗΣΤΡΑΣ

Δ. ΜΗΤΡΟΠΟΥΛΟΣ

ΣΟΛΙΣΤ

GEORGES THILL

Ἆσμα

Τὴν Κυριακὴν 17 Νοεμβρίου, ὥραν 11 π. μ.
ΓΕΝΙΚΗ ΔΟΚΙΜΗ

*Μετὰ τὴν ἔναρξιν τῆς Συναυλίας ἡ εἴσοδος θὰ ἐπιτραπῇ
μόνον κατὰ τὰ διαλείμματα.*

Τιμὴ ἀναλυτικοῦ προγράμματος: Δρ. 5.

Concert of the Athens Odeon Orchestra at the Olympia Theatre on November 18, 1935. Conductor
D. Mitropoulos, soloist Georges Thill, tenor.
(coll. S.A. Arfanis)

Viola – Βιόλα

Katims, Milton	106.
Katz, David	167, 168, 247.
Mersh, Ralph	209.
Schröer, Paul	235.

Violin – Βιολί

Corigliano, John	198.
Francescatti, Zino	16, 45, 52,100, 129, 165, 197, 251.
Goldberg, Szymon	15.
Heifetz, Jascha	17.
Krassner, Louis	204, 205, 206, 209.
Margolies, Jacques	167, 168, 247.
Menuhin, Jehudi	271.
Oistrakh, David	148, 223, 224.
Stern, Isaak	70, 163, 164.
Szigeti, Joseph	5, 25, 44, 147.
Violinist of the Minneapolis Symphony	126.
Weiss, Samuel	167, 247.

NARRATORS / ΑΦΗΓΗΤΕΣ

Kulman, Charles	156.

ORCHESTRAS / ΟΡΧΗΣΤΡΕΣ

Bavarian Radio Orchestra Munich	172, 205.
Berlin Philharmonic Orchestra	211.
Cologne Radio Orchestra	29, 113, 117,135, 137,206, 230, 235, 240, 245, 284.
Columbia Symphony Orchestra	27.
Concertgebouw Amsterdam Orchestra	3.
Detroit Symphony Orchestra	124.
International Society for Contemporary Music Concert Group	209.
Maggio Musicale Fiorentino Festival Orchestra	46,102, 143, 238, 268.

Metropolitan Opera Orchestra New York   9, 33,101, 156, 175, 176, 177, 179, 180,
181, 182, 183, 184, 241, 243, 252, 253,
263, 264, 265, 270, 272, 273, 274.

Minneapolis Symphony Orchestra   6, 7, 8, 18, 19, 23, 39, 49, 54, 55, 56,
59, 62, 66, 68, 69, 75, 77, 78, 82, 83,
85, 99,105, 107, 108, 125, 126, 128,
131, 133, 140, 141, 155, 158, 171, 186,
187, 190, 191, 192, 193, 216, 217, 228,
250, 256, 257, 260, 277, 278, 280.

NBC Symphony Orchestra   2, 25, 151, 160.

New York Philharmonic Orchestra   10,12, 24, 31,32,41,47, 48, 67, 73,76,84, 88, 92,
100, 111, 112, 115, 119, 121, 152, 157, 169,
203, 210, 215, 222, 227, 231, 232, 234, 242, 249,
254, 259, 261, 279, 281.

New York Philharmonic
Scholarship Winners Ensemble   167, 168, 247.

New York Philharmonic-Symphony Orchestra   4, 5, 11, 13, 14, 15, 16, 17, 20, 21, 22, 26, 30,
34, 35, 36, 37, 38, 40, 42, 43, 44, 50, 51, 52,
53, 57, 60, 61, 63, 64, 65, 70, 71, 72, 74, 79,
80, 81, 86, 87, 90, 91, 93, 94, 95, 96, 97, 98,
103, 104, 109, 110, 114, 116, 120, 127, 129, 130, 132,
134, 136, 138, 142, 144, 146, 147, 148, 150, 153, 154,
162, 163, 164, 165, 166, 170, 173, 185, 188, 189, 194,
195, 196, 197, 198, 199, 200, 201, 204, 207, 208, 213,
214, 218, 219, 220, 221, 223, 224, 225, 226, 229, 233,
237, 244, 246, 248, 251, 255, 258, 262, 271, 275, 276.

RAI Torino Orchestra   1, 122.

RCA Victor Symphony Orchestra   159.

Robin Hood Dell Orchestra Philadelphia   58, 123, 139, 145, 161, 178, 282, 283.

Teatro Comunale di Firenze Orchestra   174, 266, 267.

The Brass Ensemble of the Jazz &
Classical Music Society   212.

Vienna Philharmonic Orchestra   28, 45, 118, 149, 202, 236, 239, 269.

VOCALISTS / ΤΡΑΓΟΥΔΙΣΤΕΣ

THE PHILHARMONIC-SYMPHONY SOCIETY

1842 OF NEW YORK 1878

CONSOLIDATED 1928

1949 ONE HUNDRED EIGHTH SEASON **1950**

Conductors: LEOPOLD STOKOWSKI, DIMITRI MITROPOULOS
Guest Conductors: BRUNO WALTER, VICTOR DE SABATA,
LEONARD BERNSTEIN
Associate Conductor: FRANCO AUTORI

CARNEGIE HALL

SUNDAY AFTERNOON, DECEMBER 11, 1949, at 3:00

Broadcast over the Coast-to-Coast Network of the Columbia Broadcasting System

---

4772nd Concert

Under the Direction of

DIMITRI MITROPOULOS

RABAUD   Symphonic Poem, *La Procession Nocturne*, Opus 6

KRENEK   Concerto No. 3, for piano and orchestra
Allegro con passione (*Piano and brass*) —
Andante sostenuto (*Piano and strings*) —
Allegretto scherzando (*Piano and woodwinds*) —
Adagio (*Piano, harp, and percussion*) —
Vivace (*Piano and full orchestra*)
(Played without pause)
DIMITRI MITROPOULOS at *the piano*

INTERMISSION

BEETHOVEN   Symphony No. 3, E flat major, Opus 55
("Eroica")

Allegro con brio
Marcia funebre: Adagio assai
Scherzo: Allegro vivace
Finale: Allegro molto

ARTHUR JUDSON, BRUNO ZIRATO, Managers
Mr. Mitropoulos plays the Steinway Piano
THE STEINWAY is the Official Piano of The Philharmonic-Symphony Society
————*COLUMBIA AND ‡VICTOR RECORDS————

(Radio Membership Edition—Subject to Change)

Programme of the New York Philharmonic - Symphony Orchestra's concert, December 11, 1949.
(coll. Nick Nickson)

Mezzosopranos & Contraltos – Μεσόφωνοι & Κοντράλτο

Tenors – Τενόροι

Lorenz, Max	239.
McCracken, James	179, 241, 264, 265.
Majkut, Erich	239.
Mark, Peter	180, 181.
Meyer-Welfing, Hugo	269.
Mordino, Joseph	26.
Nagy, Robert	9, 243, 270.
Natali, Valiano	174.
Peerce, Jan	263.
Ristori, Brenno	174.
Schmidinger, Josef	238.
Sgarro, Louis	183, 243, 252.
Simoneau, Leopold	28, 149.
Smith-Spencer, Harvey	20.
Sullivan, Brian	241.
Tucker, Richard	180, 181, 252, 253, 264.
Wunderlich, Fritz	202.
Vinay, Ramon	241, 243, 272, 273, 275.
Zampieri, Giuseppe	118.

Baritones & Basses – Βαρύτονοι & Μπάσοι

Alden-Edkins, J	53.
Alvary, Lorenzo	241.
Anderson, Adolph	26.
Baccaloni, Salvatore	180, 183.
Bastianini, Ettore	266, 269.
Berry, Walter	149, 202.
Bierbach, Franz	269.
Boehme, Kurt	239, 272.
Braun, Hans	238.
Brownlee, John	53, 175.
Budney, Arthur	156.
Capecchi, Renato	267.
Carbonari, Virgilio	174.
Cehanovsky, George	9, 33, 175, 177, 179, 180, 181, 183, 252, 253, 265.
Christoff, Boris	266.
Corena, Fernando	149, 179, 181.
Davidson, Lawrence	175, 184, 243.
De Cesare, Luigi	176.
Doench, Karl	269.

105

APPENDIX E / ΠΑΡΑΡΤΗΜΑ Ε

Tapes of Radio Broadcasts of Dimitri Mitropoulos' concerts where most LIVE recordings come from.
Only recordings that are not yet transferred to LP or Cd are mentioned in this Appendix.
All recordings are with the New York Philharmonic Orchestra except as noted, and are listed in chronological order.

Γνωστές υπάρχουσες μαγνητοταινίες ραδιοφωνικών αναμεταδόσεων συναυλιών του Δημήτρη Μητρόπουλου, απ' όπου προέρχονται οι περισσότερες «ζωντανές» ηχογραφήσεις του.
Στο παράρτημα αυτό περιλαμβάνονται μόνο όσες απ' αυτές δεν έχουν ήδη μεταφερθεί σε δίσκους βινυλίου ή CD.
Όλες οι ηχογραφήσεις είναι με τη Φιλαρμονική Ορχήστρα της Νέας Υόρκης, εκτός αν σημειώνεται διαφορετικά, και έχουν καταχωρηθεί με χρονολογική σειρά.

29 Dec. 1940	E. Chausson
	C. Saint-Saëns
		: Poème for Violin & Orchestra Op. 25
		: Introduction & Rondo Capriccioso for Violin
		  & Orch. Op. 28
		  Albert Spalding (violin)

28 Dec. 1941	F. Busoni	: Indian Fantasy for Piano & Orchestra.
		  Egon Petri (piano)
		  2 Studies for Dr. Faust
		  Concerto for Violin & Orchestra.
		  Joseph Szigeti (violin)

22 Aug. 1943	L.v. Beethoven	: Concerto for Piano & Orchestra No 4 Op. 58 Joseph Hofmann (piano)
30 Jul. 1944	S. Rachmaninov	: The Isle of the Dead Op. 29 Symphony No 2 Op.27

20 Aug. 1944	J. Brahms	: Concerto for Violin, Cello & Orchestra Op. 102
		  John Corigliano (violin)
		  Leonard Rose (cello)
		  Symphony No 2 Op. 73

9 Dec. 1945	R. Vaughan-Williams	: Symphony No 2 "A London Symphony" Original Version with the NBC Symphony Orchestra
23 Dec. 1945	J. S. Bach	: Chorale Prelude
	A. Schönberg	: Quartet No 2 Astrid Varnay (soprano)
	E. Siegmeister	: Ozark Set with the NBC Symphony Orchestra
30 Dec. 1945	F. Couperin-D. Milhaud	: Overture & Allegro from Sonata "La Sultane"
	H. Berlioz	: King Lear Overture with the NBC Symphony Orchestra
1946	A. Schnabel	: Symphony with the Minneapolis Symphony Orchestra Recording Incomplete (Final Measures missing)
18 Dec. 1949	R. Vaughan-Williams	: Symphony No 4
1 Jan. 1950	J. Brahms	: Symphony No 4 Op. 98
8 Jan. 1950	L.v. Beethoven	: Concerto for Piano & Orchestra No 4 Op. 58 Rudolf Serkin (piano)
	R. Schumann	: Symphony No 1 Op. 38 "Spring"
15 Jan. 1950	R. Sessions	: Symphony No 2
22 Jan. 1950	L.v. Beethoven	: Symphony No 2 Op. 36
16 Apr. 1950	E. Chabrier	: Marche Joyeuse
3 Dec. 1950	H. Perpessas	: Christus Symphony
11 Mar. 1951	F. Mendelssohn	: Hebrides Overture Op. 26
	R. Schumann	: Overture, Scherzo & Finale Op. 52
	J. Sibelius	: Concerto for Violin & Orchestra Op. 47 Jascha Heifetz (violin)
1 Apr. 1951	H. Berlioz	: Rob Roy Overture
28 Oct. 1951	C. Franck-G. Pierne	: Prelude, Chorale & Fugue
	V. D' Indy	: Wallenstein Trilogy Op. 12
17 Feb. 1952	R. Vaughan-Williams	: Concerto for 2 Pianos Arthur Whittemore & Jack Lowe (pianos)
24 Feb. 1952	C. Monteverdi-O. Respighi	: L' Orfeo Charles Kullman, Frances Greer, Mack Harrell, ? Hobson, David Lloyd.
2 Mar. 1952	C. Saint-Saëns	: Symphony No 2 Op. 55
6 Apr. 1952	J. Brahms	: Concerto for Piano No 2 Op. 83 Robert Casadesus (piano)
20 Apr. 1952	J. Brahms	: Symphony No 3 Op. 90
9 Nov. 1952	D. Milhaud	: Christophe Colomb Op. 102 Dorothy Dow, Mack Harrell, Norman Scott, David Lloyd, John Brownlee

16 Nov. 1952	F. Martin	: Concerto for Violin & Orchestra Joseph Szigeti (violin)
5 Apr. 1953	H. Berlioz	: Les Nuits d' Été Op. 7 Eleanor Steber (soprano)
12 Apr. 1953	A. Berger	: Ideas of Order (World Premiere ?)
26 Apr. 1953	H. Berlioz	: Benvenuto Cellini Overture Op. 23
18 Oct. 1953	G. v. Einem	: Capriccio
15 Nov. 1953	R. Schumann F. Mendelssohn	: Symphony No 1 Op. 38 "Spring" : Concerto for Violin & Orchestra Op. 64 Misha Elman (violin)
22 Nov. 1953	J. Brahms	: Symphony No 4 Op. 98
29 Nov. 1953	L. v Beethoven M. Ravel	: Symphony No 2 Op. 36 : Concerto for Piano & Orchestra in G major Nicole Henriot Schweitzer (piano)
18 Apr. 1954	J. S. Bach	: Suite No 3 for Orchestra BWV 1068
25 Apr. 1954	E. Lalo S. Rachmaninov	: Le Roi D' Ys Overture : Concerto for Piano & Orchestra No 4 Op. 40 Leonid Hambro (piano)
2 May 1954	A. Glazounov	: Concerto for Violin & Orchestra Op. 82 Michael Rabin (violin)
10 Oct. 1954	C. M. v Weber	: Der Freischütz Overture
27 Feb. 1955	S. Rachmaninov	: Vocalise Op. 34, No 14
3 Apr. 1955	P. Ladmirault	: Variations on a biniou air
10 Apr. 1955	C. M. v Weber	: Der Freischütz Overture

On Tour in Seattle

8 May 1955	D. Kabalevsky	: Colas Breugnon Overture Op. 24 (not broadcast)

At The Athens Festival (Orfeo Theatre Athens, Greece)

1 Oct. 1955	R. Schumann D. Shostakovich	: Symphony No 2 in C major Op. 61 : Symphony No 10 in e minor Op. 93

At The Athens Festival (Orfeo Theatre Athens, Greece)

(with an introduction by Dimitri Mitropoulos
announcing the program of this concert.)

2 Oct. 1955	G. Verdi J. Brahms N. Skalkottas L. v Beethoven	: La Forza del Destino Overture : Variations on a Theme by Haydn Op. 56a : Four Greek Dances : Symphony No 3 Op. 55 "Eroica"
6 Nov. 1955	W. A. Mozart	: Concerto for Piano & Orchestra No 22 KV 482 Pietro Scarpini (piano)

ΔΗΜΟΣ ΑΘΗΝΑΙΩΝ

ΘΕΡΙΝΑΙ ΣΥΝΑΥΛΙΑΙ

ΕΙΣ ΤΑΣ ΣΥΝΟΙΚΙΑΣ ΤΩΝ ΑΘΗΝΩΝ

ΧΟΡΗΓΙΑ ΤΟΥ ΔΗΜΟΥ ΑΘΗΝΑΙΩΝ

ΣΕΙΡΑ ΤΡΙΤΗ

ΠΛΑΤΕΙΑ ΑΚΡΟΠΟΛΕΩΣ

~~ΔΕΥΤΕΡΑ 5~~ ΑΥΓΟΥΣΤΟΥ 1935, ὥραν 7.30′ μ.μ.

ΤΕΤΑΡΤΗ 7

ΤΡΙΤΗ ΣΥΝΑΥΛΙΑ

ΕΚΤΕΛΕΣΤΑΙ:

Η ΣΥΜΦΩΝΙΚΗ ΟΡΧΗΣΤΡΑ

ΤΟΥ ΩΔΕΙΟΥ ΑΘΗΝΩΝ

ΕΞ 90 ΜΟΥΣΙΚΩΝ

Ὑπὸ τὴν Διεύθυνσιν

τοῦ κ. **Δ. ΜΗΤΡΟΠΟΥΛΟΥ**

Ἐντελῶς δωρεάν.—Οὐδεμία ὑπερτίμησις θὰ ἐπιτραπῇ εἰς τὰ πέριξ Κέντρα.—Οὔτε ἐνοικίασις καθισμάτων.

Open air concert of the Athens Odeon Orchestra conducted by D. Mitropoulos at the Acropolis Square, Athens August 7, 1935.
(coll. S. A. Arfanis)

19 Feb. 1956	E. Bloch	: Schelomo for Cello & Orchestra Op. 33
		Laszlo Varga (cello)
	S. Rachmaninov	: Concerto for Piano & Orchestra No 3 Op. 30
		Witold Malkuzynski (piano)
29 Apr. 1956	S. Prokofiev	: Concerto for Violin & Orchestra No 2 Op. 63
		Zino Francescatti (violin)
21 Oct. 1956	L.v Beethoven	: Symphony No 5 Op. 67
4 Nov. 1956	E. Lalo	: Symphonie Espagnole for Violin & Orchestra Op. 21
		Betty Jean Hagen (violin)
11 Nov. 1956	P. I. Tchaikovsky	: Concerto for Piano & Orchestra No 1 Op. 23
		Anna Xydi-Antoniades (piano)
5 May 1957	W. Walton	: Concerto for Cello & Orchestra
		Gregor Piatigorsky (cello)
12 May 1957	Z. Kodály	: Psalmus Hungaricus Op. 13
		David Lloyd (tenor)
	L. Foss	: Psalms for Chorus & Orchestra
13 Oct. 1957	A. Vivaldi	: Concerto in g minor
3 Nov. 1957	S. Prokofiev	: Romeo & Juliet Ballet Op. 64 (excerpts)
	D. Kabalevsky	: Symphony No 4 (US Premiere)
2 Feb. 1958	W. A. Mozart	: Concerto for Violin & Orchestra No 3 KV 216
		Leonid Kogan (violin)

At The Salzburg Festival

10 Aug. 1958	J. Brahms	: Symphony No 3 Op. 90
	R. Strauss	: Also Sprach Zarathustra op. 30
		with the Concertgebouw Orchestra Amsterdam
2 Jan. 1960	L.v Beethoven	: Grosse Fuge Op. 133 for Orchestra
9 Jan. 1960	A. Bliss	: Concerto for Piano & Orchestra
		Gina Bachauer (piano)

At The Vienna Festival ?

| 28 Sep. 1960 | G. Mahler | : Symphony No 9 |
| | | with The Concertgebouw Orchestra Amsterdam ? |

Miscellaneous

18 Mar. 1949		: Minneapolis Farewell Speech
Mar. 1950		: D. Mitropoulos rehearsing the third movement -Mephistopheles- of F. Liszt's A Faust Symphony, excerpt from 20th Century Fox film "Of Men & Music", directed by Irving Reis. (1951 release)
1952 ?		: Interview in Iowa
1954 ?		: Interview by Lee Eitzen
?		: D. Mitropoulos, "This I believe"
?		: Interview by Jim Fassett on CBS Radio